"THE WONDERFUL
WRITING MACHINE"

By BRUCE BLIVEN, JR.

Compliments of the Royal Typewriter Company
whose combined effort with Random House, the
publisher, made this book possible.

Royal, World's Largest Manufacturer of Typewriters, has long known the impact that the typewriter has had on the business and writing world
as the most versatile of communication instruments.
This book was written with the hope that the history
and development of this wonderful invention would
be more fully understood.

ROYAL TYPEWRITER COMPANY, INC.
2 Park Avenue, New York 16, New York

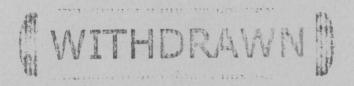

The Wonderful Writing Machine

Bruce Bliven, Jr.

THE WONDERFUL
WRITING MACHINE

Random House  New York

To Naomi

Acknowledgments

FOR complete freedom to explore its offices, factories and files, along with permission to interrupt its busy personnel with my often foolish questions, I owe thanks to the Royal Typewriter Company. I am grateful in particular to Fortune P. Ryan, Allan A. Ryan, Carl Mc-Kelvy, Gordon G. Ackland, C. B. Cook, Julius Schillinger, Stella Willins, John Forshay, H. C. Draper, Wayne K. Boulton, Russell Risbey, Xavier N. Benziger, C. B. Cook, Jr., E. J. Cichowitz, Thomas Kayser, Allan S. Cook, Gilbert F. Berry, LeRoy T. Martin and Horace Stapenell, among many others. I am indebted to the staff of the New York Public Library and to Milton Kaplan of the Library of Congress; and to Robert N. Linscott, Saxe Commins and Ray Freiman of Random House; and to my literary agent, Jeanne Hale.

Parts of this book have appeared in the *Atlantic Monthly* and *Collier's* and are reprinted by the permission of their editors.

B.B.Jr.

Picture Credits

Contents

Illustrations

xiii

The Wonderful Writing Machine

---

1 / Girl in the Office

You hear the word "secretary" and the image that flashes through your mind is a girl in an office who types for her living.

That's not far wrong. In the United States there are about two and a half million such girls—or ladies, to be more polite and to take proper account of the fact that nearly half of them are married women. There are more women working at typing than at anything else; twice as many, for instance, as are selling in stores and shops and six times the number working on farms (not counting farmers' wives).

Your only mistake—and to call it a mistake is almost a quibble—is that you've forgotten that men (even boys) can also be secretaries. Nearly a million men are employed in that capacity. To say that they are "forgotten" is to put a better face on their plight than the facts warrant, for they have never been remembered except during a brief period when the writing machine itself was in its infancy. The National Office Management Association, along with its other work, is engaged in a campaign to give the word "secretary" a more precise meaning, but the idea

3

A Demonstrator at Work With the Alfred E. Beach Typewriter, 1856

---

is not to make the term seem more masculine. (Nobody is working on that angle except a few unorganized male secretaries who, on the whole, feel that they're licked at the start.) What the NOMA wants the world to understand is that "secretary" is a specific job classification. It should not be confused with "typist," "junior stenographer" or "stenographer," for, properly speaking, a "secretary" is more than any of these. A "typist" of either sex knows the touch system but not shorthand. A "junior stenographer" knows shorthand as well as typing and can take and transcribe dictation. A "stenographer" is proficient in all these skills and also knows letter forms, the various office systems and clerical tasks, like filing, related to the job. Finally, a "secretary" knows everything a senior stenographer knows and can also relieve the boss of some of his routine work.

Above and beyond "secretary," according to the NOMA's recommended terminology, there is the "private secretary" who works directly with an executive in a close, confidential capacity, has considerable experience, and is competent to stand in for her (or his) boss when he (or she) is not around.

"Private secretary" is as important as a typewriter operator can get. Beyond that eminence—if, indeed, there is any such beyond—a lady is in line for a secretary-typist of her own.

Despite the NOMA's worthy efforts to purify the language, a good many persons are all mixed up about these terms. Male secretaries are likely to be called "clerks." And all young ladies in offices, including clerks, receptionists, vice-presidents and executive directors, are occasionally mistaken for secretaries whether or not the error is flattering. Yet there is little confusion on one point. The typewriter operator, and, in particular, the female typewriter operator, is a terrific power. Her take-home pay, in many cases, is less than $50 a week, but she has got the average business office, not to mention the average business-man, lawyer, doctor and government official, under fairly good control. The basic tool of business communication is in her hands. Although the telephone is steadily growing in impor-tance, the typewritten letter and the typewritten memo remain the primary means men of affairs have for telling each other what they think. The typewritten record is their memory. The typewritten contract is their instrument of agreement. Further-more, the secretary has wisely seized control of the telephone in addition to the writing machine, following the strategy dear to the hearts of Old Bolsheviks. She makes two or three calls for every one of the boss's. She screens all his incoming calls, allow-ing him to receive only those she deems suitable. And she gets his numbers for him, often fighting his battles in the process if another secretary answers and challenges on the delicate point of who shall speak first to whom. In short, American business is conducted at the pace the American secretary sets, or something between forty and seventy words per minute.

Her importance as a typist, however, is hardly more than the first paragraph of her full story. Most Americans are too young to recall what the business world was like before the female entered it and revolutionized its *mores*. The girl secretary led the invasion. Before the last two decades of the nineteenth century offices in the downtown districts of cities were filled entirely with men, many of them wearing their hats indoors and spitting into brass containers called cuspidors which stood on rubber mats on the floor. Offices almost never had rugs, and the air, which was changed as seldom as possible, smelled of cigar smoke. Instead of being decorated, offices were hammered together by carpenters. The dominant esthetic idea was to get in as much oak as possible in the form of railings and paneling and to keep everything good and dark so it wouldn't matter how much dirt accumulated. The concept of the clean desk top had not yet been invented. Most executives used roll-top desks. The more important the man, the bigger his desk, and the bigger the desk the more weird pigeonholes and mysterious little drawers it had; an executive could lose an entire season's worth of documents inside a jumbo roll-top without ever getting up from his chair. He felt no guilt about messiness. If the working surface became overwhelmed with random correspondence, newspaper clippings, or fishing-equipment catalogues, all he had to do was roll down the top, hiding everything in one sweeping motion, and walk away. He either wrote his own letters in longhand in pen and ink, or summoned a young man to take shorthand dictation and transcribe, later, in longhand. At the end of the day, the office boys took all the originals and, by wetting them with evil-smelling felt cloths and then pressing the damp

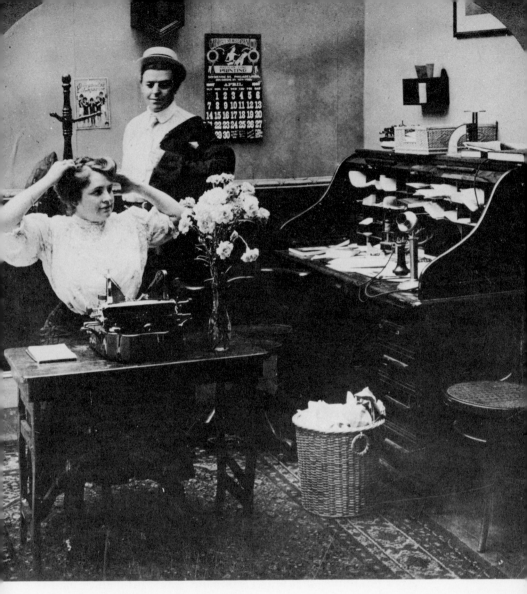

The Fashionable Typist of 1907

letters against the pages of a book, made one copy of each for
the record. Then they quickly folded them, put them in en-
velopes, and raced with them to the post office, hoping that no
one would have time to notice that the copy press had turned

the originals into illegible smears. The business district had no sandwich shoppes or drug-store lunch counters. It might have a few restaurants where ladies (visitors) were invited. Most men ate lunch in the omnipresent bars which gave away a substantial amount of food for free, if anybody had a thought of actually eating. It was as hard to find a crisp salad or a chocolate walnut sundae with whipped cream as it was to buy a hair ribbon.

The female typewriter operator and the other members of her sex who followed her into the downtown area got rid of nearly all of that in remarkably short order. Their influence did not stop, however, at the boundaries of the business section. When, practically overnight, a new occupational group appeared in the Bureau of the Census tabulations ("Clerical and kindred workers, female"), nearly everybody with something to sell began to examine its members' tastes, opinions, habits and hopes with greedy earnestness. The typewriter manufacturers, for good and obvious reasons, were the first to sense that the girls in offices were worth serious consideration. Not more than a short half-step behind came the office-desk, posture-chair, and business-supplies industries. And on their heels were nearly all others except a few, like the cuspidor interests, who saw that they were doomed. It was soon apparent that the secretary was far more than a secretary. She was, in the aggregate, a symbol of all young women with more than average education who had enterprise enough to go out, learn a skill, and make some money. She was a pace-setter and a style-maker, with influence far out of proportion to her actual numbers. The garment industry noticed that when she bought shirtwaists to wear to work, shirtwaists became a big mail-order item for farmers' daughters who had never typed a letter in their lives. Hat manufacturers saw that, if she took to wearing her hair in a bun at the back, millions of other women could be expected to follow suit.

Today's secretary is in the same position as her 1890 counterpart, only more so. Because she's always short of time, she's the first to experiment with frozen waffles that fit into her pop-up toaster. When Paris says skirts will shorten, and the United States waits in suspense to see whether the edict will be obeyed, the young businesswoman's hem, or knees, determine the outcome. Every other secretary is married in 1954, so that she also decides whether tweed is the popular fabric for sofa upholstering and how big television screens should be. She is the epitome of that class of buyers receptive to the newest and most stylish; advertisers and sales organizations have her squarely in their sights and are helplessly dependent upon her whims.

Part of her power, paradoxically, lies in her intention to quit being a secretary. She may plan to go on from typing into executive, or management, or editorial work, or any of the many jobs of infinite variety that are now possible for her, including banking and play production. Or she may expect to retire when she gets married or as soon as her husband is earning enough by

A Typical Office Scene, 1900

himself to keep her in the style she has helped pay for. Neither dream is hopeless. A good many of the top business and professional women in the country began by typing and transcribing dictation, and only 27 per cent of all married women hold jobs, although the latter figure has been showing a steady rise. In any case, the average female typewriter operator abandons her job after about three years.

This adds to the secretary's importance in two ways. It enlarges her scope as a buyer of the nation's products. Crib manufacturers and diaper-service salesmen are forced to realize that, despite her temporary occupational status, she may be about to become a housewife and mother; urban landlords must recognize that, in virtually no time, or on the expiration of the lease, she may lead the family out of the city apartment to Pleasantvista, where the schools are not so crowded. In the second place, since the average secretary's working life is short, there are seldom enough of her to go around.

In Denver, Colorado, last summer, to choose a random example, the Barnes School of Commerce, with a graduating class of ten, had calls for 128 girls. The secretarial shortage is acute as a normal thing, excepting only the worst months of the worst recessions and depressions. It was about as bad in late 1953 as it has ever been. It has been exceedingly bad for more than a decade, since early in World War II when the gag originated about the hiring officer for one government agency who put a washing machine, a typewriter, and a machine gun beside his desk and, as long as a secretarial applicant could identify the typewriter within a reasonable time limit, she got a job. The Sunday *New York Times* recently carried forty-seven columns of "Help Wanted—Female" classified advertising, in almost every case calling for women with a knowledge of typing. New York City was well off, from a secretary-supply point of view, compared to the West and Southwest. Chicago businessmen thought they were having a tough time, but in Houston, Texas, when employers heard how easy the Chicago situation was compared to their own, they found it hard to believe. (The *average* weekly salary for a fully qualified private secretary in Houston was $76; and a good many were getting as much as $100.) Los Angeles, Baton Rouge and Tulsa were as short as Houston, perhaps a little more so.

One might assume that under these circumstances the secretarial-school business would be in superlative shape, for graduates of the famous firms like Packard and Katherine Gibbs can waltz into the best jobs with the minimum difficulty. (The Boston branch of Gibbs had an average of twenty-five requests per girl for its graduating class of June, 1953.) But in fact, while business and secretarial schools have been doing moderately well, the severe shortage does not assist them: a fumbler can fare so well in the job market that she loses the incentive to become a virtuoso. In Detroit, not long ago, for instance, a couple of girls who had learned to type about thirty-five words a minute in their high-school class enrolled in a postgraduate secretarial school, figuring that they ought to be able to go nearly twice that fast before they began to look for work. They never got a chance to hear the first day's lecture, for they were both hired, at good salaries, before the course began. The current shortage of secretaries would be less severe if more babies had been born during the depression 'thirties. Hard times held down the birth rate, depriving the business world (and the labor market as a whole) of a good many girls who would now be in the prime of secretarial life. It will be twelve more years before the baby boom of 1946–1948 begins to work as a counteracting influence.

No matter what they tell their wives, business and professional men like their secretaries young and they like them pretty. They may not get what they want. They may need a stenographer-typist so badly that they are forced to employ a young man. But there is no sense in pretending that Marilyn Monroe would have a hard time finding secretarial employment provided that she promised to study shorthand and the touch system. A vintage vaudeville skit that was first played before the turn of the century was aimed at the heart of the matter. A dazzlingly beautiful doll walks into the lawyer's office. "Tell me," the lawyer says, "can you take dictation?" "Yes," the doll says, lifting her eyebrows ever so slightly, "or I can leave it alone."

Yet for at least two generations after the first secretaries went to work, the nation, for obscure reasons of its own, preferred to pretend that sex had nothing to do with the sensational popularity of female typewriter operators. All sorts of explanations were offered: women were said to have a peculiar aptitude for work requiring finger dexterity, and to be more conscientious than men, and better custodians of confidential business secrets. Thousands of words—pamphlets, books and magazine articles—were written about the path to success as a secretary. Almost without exception the authors recommended modesty in dress and manners; taste and neatness, but no flash. In the early fiction written with secretaries for heroines, the hero (a rising young executive in the firm) was usually so impressed by his secretary's decorum that he didn't dare even to propose; in one story after another he called her in and dictated a proposal, building to the climax in which she, her eyes brimming with tears, asked, "And to whom, sir, is this missive to be addressed?" In spite of a certain obbligato of joking and snickering that has always attended the subject, the view that the female typewriter operator is hired for her letter-writing efficiency alone has shown great staying power. As early as 1904, J. Charles Groshur, who worked for a secretarial employment agency, reported to *The Typewriter Trade Journal* that nine out of ten calls he received asked for female secretaries, not male, and generally in "most peculiar language," like, "Have you got a pretty blonde?" Yet as late as 1953 it was possible to stir up quite a fuss, as did Bernice Fitz-Gibbon, the brilliant advertising woman, by saying to an audience made up of the deans of women and placement-

---

Today's Secretary. She Sets the Pace of Business at between 40 and 70 Words Per Minute

office heads from more than a hundred colleges: "Preoccupation with pulchritude on the part of the employer may not be noble and high-minded, but it is a fact. It's sex. You can't fight it. But you might develop a few slogans to put over your more exciting products, such as, 'Here's Holyoke's Hottest—Handle with Asbestos Gloves' . . . or, 'Smith Girls Are Girlier Girls'."

Considering her vast power, her far-reaching influence, and her strong bargaining position, today's typewriter operator is entitled to a measure of smug self-satisfaction. She belongs to the largest, strongest group of working women in the world; her political, economic and social status is unparalleled in the stormy history of the fight for women's rights. Her competence has won her nearly all the political equality that the suffragettes, like the Englishwoman, Emily Davison, who rushed onto the Epsom race course on Derby Day to try to stop the King's horse and was trampled to death, thought only militant action could achieve. Yet according to a recent poll of the twelve thousand members of the National Secretaries Association, Miss Secretary, 1954, is about as contented with her lot as a wet hen.

The association asked its members, "What are your boss's worst faults?" (The form of the question in itself was revealing; it excluded the possibility that the boss might be faultless.) The respondents were virtually unanimous: "He forgets to tell me in advance about his plans." When the boss decides to catch the noon plane to Chicago, or take off the afternoon, or work until midnight, his right-hand girl and confidential assistant is the last one to hear about it. But that's only the beginning of a secretary's troubles. Among lesser grievances was executive procrastination; the scoundrels try never to dictate anything in the morning that can be put off until the afternoon; and transcribing, needless to say, can't begin until dictation is done. One favorite boss trick is to loaf around all day, talking on the telephone to old college friends until 4:45 P.M., and then, as he reaches for his own hat and coat, he rips off a couple of letters, asking sweetly that they go out, if possible, before five. His dictating technique, furthermore, leaves room for improvement. He mumbles. He talks with pencils, paper clips, rubber bands and eyeglass frames in his mouth. He interjects all sorts of extraneous grunts, gasps for air and tentative noises ("Ennn-nngh," "errrrrrrh," "aaaangh"). He forgets what he has just said. Often, when it is read back to him, he acts as if he can't imagine where it came from, and revises completely. In a good many cases, he regards, ". . . and so on—you finish it up—just keep this character happy, but tell him firmly, 'No' " as a reasonable substitute for saying whatever it is he has been trying to say. But in contrast to his other mental inadequacies, he is a genius at inventing nonsecretarial tasks for his secretary to perform. He may ask her to read and summarize a boring book over her weekend so that he'll have something to say at *his* boss's dinner party. Or to see whether, during her lunch hour, she can't pick up a little something for his mother-in-law's birthday. It's bad enough to do his personal errands, but doing his wife's chores is a notch lower on the scale. Lowest of all is filling in for his wife in business-social engagements—lunch with the Wichita sales manager and his wife—so dreadful that Mrs. Boss has absolutely refused to have anything to do with it. But who, come Christmas time, gets the mink stole? Exactly. All Miss Secretary can expect is the gift-wrapped bottle of toilet water. And, since she had to pick it out for herself, she didn't have the heart to shoot the works and get the two-ounce flacon of Joy.

"I feel that I have done something for the women who have always had to work so hard," wrote Christopher Latham Sholes, whose typewriter was the first to be manufactured and marketed commercially. Despite the secretaries' list of harassments, frustrations and subtle tortures, there is evidence that Sholes's feeling was not wrong, and that even the women themselves will admit it. About the same time that the NSA was collecting its devastating data, one hundred bright-eyed young ladies at Packard Junior College were being asked why they were taking a secretarial course; or, in effect, why were they ambitious to become typist-stenographers? "We think it will be very interesting work," they said, first off. And then they added that the training was quick and inexpensive; that it offered a stepping stone to other careers, paid well, offered advancement, and that the field was not too crowded. Typing and shorthand, the students felt, were skills that a girl could fall back on in later years, if necessary, because they were not too strenuous physically. And, in addition, they considered them useful in personal life as well as means to a career.

None of the one hundred young ladies, of course, had had any experience in the cruel, hard world. None had ever tried to cope with a mumbling, thoughtless, forgetful employer. Therefore the results of the questionnaire were shown to fifty experienced secretaries, veterans who really knew the facts. What did the professionals think of the fledglings' optimism? They thought that the young ladies were just about right.

2 / The Wonderful Writing Machine

Sitting on her desk in front of today's secretary is an extraordinary device, the typewriter, a key-operated machine designed to print the letters of the alphabet, the numerals, one or two fractions, and the common punctuation marks one after another in a fair imitation of the work produced by the far larger and heavier printing press.

The young lady would not be where she is if the typewriter had never been invented.

This is a notion so boring, to her way of thinking, that she seldom lets it cross her mind. Yet it would be entirely fitting if, from time to time, she could give her writing machine some small attention, like wiping off the dust or whisking the bits of eraser away from the printing point. Women are not wholly unresponsive to the charms of mere machinery. Some of them, meeting in the supermarket, discuss electric washing machines in the most extravagant terms of praise. Yet, worthy as the washing machine is, it has played practically no part in the

17

Today's Typewriter

extension of woman suffrage. Automobiles are admired by women who, if we are to believe the advertisements, enjoy picking out gay materials and bright colors for their interiors; yet the automobile has brought few women (apart from a handful of lady taxi drivers) economic self-sufficiency. Typewriter manufacturers have done everything they could think of to please the fair sex, yet for every woman who praises their thoughtfulness and ingenuity, a thousand women maintain complete silence on the subject. They are more likely to compliment the simple and essentially brutelike garbage-disposal device than the complex and marvelously delicate typewriter.

Men are no better than women. They are slightly less in the typewriter's debt as far as their personal status is concerned, to be sure. But men are supposed to be endowed with superior mechanical aptitude, or at least to acquire an interest in machines in conformity with our cultural pattern. Men do warm at the sight of outboard motors, guns, cameras and gadgets that enable them to practice golf shots indoors. Some build radios and television sets as a hobby. A good many can take a clock apart and put it together. But except for those professionals who make it their business, men do not know what to do about a broken typewriter.

In eighty years the typewriter has revolutionized communications, helped in the dramatic expansion of business, increased profits by decreasing the cost of making them, freed mankind from the drudgery and illegibility of handwriting, saved incalculable hours of time, transformed the appearance of offices, given birth to a myriad of related and dependent business machines, influenced the language and changed the methods of primary education. The names of the great typewriter inventors —Burt, Sholes, Crandall, Hammond, Hess and the rest—should be as familiar as Fulton, Whitney, Morse and Edison. To the average schoolboy they mean nothing at all.

In the view of one expert, a typewriter repairman whose territory includes the heart of midtown Manhattan, the explanation is simple enough: "Typewriters are too good for people. They last too long. They work too well. If they were a lot more trouble than they are, typists would be more interested in them." A sales executive for one of the major typewriter companies sees the phenomenon in different terms. "There's little pride of ownership involved," he said recently, "and no one hungers for a typewriter. Typing is a habit, all right, but no craving develops. The customer can face not having a typewriter without fear. He certainly doesn't imagine that non-ownership is a hidden disease. In fact, the real customer is the

secretary, and she is not actually the buyer at all." Their language and perspectives may differ, but both men are talking about the same thing: the world, for the most part, takes the writing machine for granted.

Fortunately, if only for the sake of the morale of the tens of thousands of persons engaged in the typewriter industry, the picture is not completely black. Some men and women love typewriters dearly. A small but growing number of them collect old typewriters as antiques. A few take pride, as hobbyists, in restoring decrepit machines to writing condition, a peaceful version of the perilous fad of driving around in ancient, rebuilt automobiles. In addition, a somewhat larger class of typewriter fanciers feels irresistibly drawn by the sight of a machine. In stores where typewriters are on display, its members are unable to pass by without sidling up to the counter and trying a sentence or two, usually "Now is the time for all good men to come to the aid of their party." And these typewriter fans are energetic in trying to think up good reasons to turn in their old machines for the new models.

Even among typewriter admirers, however, there are comparatively few who appreciate the machine's intrinsic merit. They understand that a typewriter's insides are complicated without knowing that it has more than two thousand separate parts—some of them machined to tolerances of within seven-tenths of a thousandth of an inch—that have been assembled almost entirely by hand; or that the assembly involves something in the neighborhood of five thousand distinct operations. They realize that a typewriter can be adjusted, but not that virtually all of its working parts require precision setting, and have been set, in the factory, by the expenditure of hours of

Percy Smock of Redwood City, California, with a Few Antiques from his Large Collection

skilled craftsmen's time. The typewriter makes almost any other one of the familiar gadgets of our lives look absurdly simple. And yet, with a modicum of care, it is among the most reliable.

On another, more practical level, both men and women prove they do think more of the typewriter than they let themselves know: they buy them. Almost every place of business has one. Some have thousands. In millions of homes the typewriter is really as important as the washing machine; it's just that the members of the family seldom think of mentioning that fact. A young man or woman would hardly consider going off to college without a portable. (Sometimes the same machine that Father used, with the tattered remnants of the school colors still sticking to the battered case.) And—perhaps the ultimate test— when man goes into war he keeps his typewriter close by his side. The captain of a battleship insists that there be fifty-five typewriters on board before he feels fully equipped to meet the enemy. On the ground, as the army moves forward, there are

The Typewriter as a War Weapon. Canadian Light Artillery, World War I

more writing machines within four thousand yards of the front lines than medium and light artillery pieces combined.

The three and a half million secretaries (male and female) don't gush about the machine ordinarily, because they are professionals. Like other professionals they look upon the tools of their trade with a certain mixture of emotions. But whether or not they care at all about typewriter history or the niceties of typewriter manufacture, they can tell the good typewriters from the bad. They decide what the office machine shall be. And, since the office typewriter is dominant—the portable is merely its baby brother—they set the specifications for the whole industry. What secretaries like best are good typewriters. Their preference is law.

3 / Burt's Necessity

It took a lot of inventing to provide the secretary with her machine.

A prominent English engineer, Henry Mill, was the first, as far as anybody knows, to think up the basic idea of a typewriter. Queen Anne granted him a Royall Letters Patent on January 7, 1714. It gave Mill exclusive rights, for the next fourteen years, to

> an artificial machine or method for the impressing or transcribing of letters singly or progressively one after another, as in writing, whereby all writings whatsoever may be engrossed in paper or parchment so neat and exact as not to be distinguished from print; that the said machine or method may be of great use in settlements and publick records, the impression being deeper and more lasting than any other writing, and not to be erased or counterfeited without manifest discovery.

Mill presumably made a model, for the reference to erasing sounds like the comment of a man who had actually written the wrong thing and had struggled, like all the typists who followed him during the succeeding two and a half centuries, to rub it out. There are no drawings of Mill's machine, however, and because our national pride is wounded by the thought that an English-man should have invented a predominantly American gadget, his invention has taken a lot of abuse. Some grumblers have said that Mill never built a typewriter at all, but merely patented an idea. Others claim that while he may have built something, it was not a true typewriter but an embossing device to help the blind. Feeble rationalizations at best. And a waste of time. Because if it wasn't Mill who invented the first typewriter, it was either Von Knaus or Count Reipperg of Vienna, in the early 1760's, or a Swiss, Louis Jacquet, in 1780. Or a Frenchman, Pingeron, who invented a writing machine in 1784 that *was* designed to emboss letters for the blind to read with their finger tips, as he was the first to admit. Or the Italian, Pellegrino Turri di Castelnuovo, who invented a similar gadget in 1808 with a specific blind lady in mind, the Countess Carolina Fantoni da Fivizzono. Or another Italian, Pietro Conti of Cilavenga, whose 1823 typewriter, according to his own claim, wrote "fast and clear enough for anyone, even those with bad sight."

Since there's no real chance of arguing that a United States citizen originated the typewriter idea, we might just as well admit that Mill was first, and be thankful that he was not a Russian. (The first Russian typewriter, no matter what the Russian history books may say by now, was invented by Jaan Jaackson in Riga in about 1840.)

The first American typewriter was invented by William Austin Burt of Mount Vernon, Michigan, a village just north of Detroit, during the winter of 1828–1829. It was patented on July 23, 1829.

Burt was an amazing man. Inventing the typewriter was a minor achievement, as he saw it. He was busy, at the moment, with a whole lot of other projects. He had more paper work than

William Austin Burt (1792–1858)

he could manage. So he simply invented a typewriter, casually, to save himself time. He didn't think it was anything to get particularly excited about—although some of his friends did, and his children and grandchildren grew increasingly appreciative of his ingenuity as they contemplated the fortune he did not make out of it.

Burt was excited about a great many things throughout his life, however, especially astronomy, navigation and surveying. He was born in 1792 on his father's farm at Petersham, Massachusetts. It was not much of a farm. His father sold it in 1802 and moved west to Freehold, New York, hoping to do better; and shortly thereafter he sold the new place and moved to Broadalbin, New York. By the time he was twelve years old, William Austin had had nearly all the formal schooling he was ever going to get, but it by no means satisfied his hunger for knowledge. When he wasn't doing his share of the farm work, along with his eight brothers and sisters, he read books. Books about the sea, when he could get them. All his immediate ancestors on both sides of the family had been seafaring men. His mother, whose father had been lost at sea, took a dim view of sailing as a way of life. She persuaded William Austin not to go to sea, a couple of years later, but there was nothing she could do to keep him from being fascinated by the subject. One of Burt's chores was making roof shingles. His first invention, at the age of twelve, was a book-holder which enabled him to use both hands to work on the shingles with a drawshave without having to stop reading about ships and sailors.

Like all compulsive readers, Burt had trouble finding sufficient reading material. He owned a pretty good manual on navigation and a mathematics textbook and several farm almanacs, but for a long time he lacked an astronomy book. The navigation manual's text had some helpful clues, however, and the almanacs offered suggestive sun and moon tables; Burt did pretty well figuring out what he'd learn from an astronomy book if he could ever lay his hands on one. At fourteen, following a line drawing in the navigation manual, he built himself a sextant, although he had never seen a real one, and accurately computed the latitude and longitude of the Burt farm, helped by the fact that it stood still instead of sailing on like a full-rigged ship, but sorry, undoubtedly, that that was the case.

Burt got interested in surveying, which was a little bit like navigating on land, after his mother talked him out of pursuing a seagoing career. He acquired a broken, second-hand, magnetic surveying compass, fixed it up, and began running surveys around Erie County as a semi-pro, helping farmers figure out just exactly where their land ended and the next farm began. He married Phoebe Cole in 1813, served 120 days as a soldier in the New York Militia during the War of 1812, and then he tried working for his father-in-law, who was a merchant. That was no good. He tried working for his brother-in-law, who, as a contractor, built flour mills and sawmills. That was better. But it was not exactly what Burt wanted. In 1817 Burt took a long, difficult, exploratory trip down Lake Erie to see how things looked farther west. Compared to the rosy pictures the land speculators in Buffalo were painting, things didn't look so hot. Burt came home. He thought about Michigan for five years. In 1822 he went out a second time, planning to get himself set as a surveyor, if possible, and a house built, and then go back and bring his family with him. He headed for Detroit, a busy town with a population of almost fifteen hundred, an important trading post and a rendezvous point for streams of emigrants headed still farther west.

The Michigan peninsula was just getting popular. The land agents in the East, with acreage to sell in northern Ohio, Indiana and Illinois, had persuaded many persons that Michigan north of Detroit was a repulsive swamp, impassable except in winter when it froze over, and not worth a homesteader's consideration. By 1822, however, the anti-Michigan talk was losing effectiveness, for those who had settled in the area were sending back word that those were not swamps but charming lakes. Or, as Michigan's singularly unaggressive state motto (compared, for instance, to Alabama's "We Dare Defend Our Rights," or New Hampshire's "Live Free or Die") declares, "If you seek a pleasant peninsula, look around you." (*Si quaeris peninsulam amoenam circumspice.*)

Burt's "Typographer," Made in the Woods of Michigan, 1829

Burt looked around and picked a home site at Mount Vernon. He found a few surveying jobs, but not enough, so he was forced back into flour-mill and sawmill building, as before. He had his own log house in fairly good shape by 1824. He went and got Phoebe and his boys right away, and brought them there to live in it, although he still had a lot of improving and clearing to do. In 1826 he was elected to the Territorial Legislative Council. It all added up to far more paper work—contracts, correspondence, reports, records and statements—than a busy man could handle. Something had to be done about it.

That was when he thought of a writing machine. He went to the office of his friend, John P. Sheldon, who was the founder and editor of the *Michigan Gazette* (later the *Detroit Free*

Press) and got an assortment of type. Burt took it home to his workshop-shed and began building the first model of what he called a "typographer." It was a heavy, boxlike affair, made almost entirely of wood. Its principle was like that of the familiar toy typewriter; the type was mounted on a rotating, semicircular frame, not on individual type bars, and the idea was to move the wheel around until the desired letter came to the printing point. Then it was pressed down against the paper with a lever. Ink was supplied by two inking pads, one on either side of the printing point. The typographer wrote on a long strip of paper. After you had typed a full page, you tore off the sheet, like a paper towel, and you could tell when you had filled a page by watching a paper-measuring gadget, a modified clock face and indicator-pointer on the front of the box. All things considered, the typographer did good work, especially after you'd gotten the hang of it. The print was neat and eminently legible. From Burt's point of view, it had just one serious flaw; writing with the typographer was slightly slower than writing with the pen.

Not only had Burt lost ground in his battle with his backlog of correspondence, but as soon as Sheldon laid eyes on the device he steamed up with enthusiasm, and his optimism resulted in still more paper work for Burt; before long the old unwritten letters that had been the mother of the invention seemed few compared to the new ones. Sheldon immediately began thinking in long-range, high-pressure terms. He sat right down, on May 25, 1829, and wrote a letter to the President of the United States, Andrew Jackson:

> Sir:
>
> This is a specimen of the printing done by me on Mr. Burt's typographer. You will observe some inaccuracies in the situation of the letters; these are owing to the imperfections of the machine, it having been made in the woods of Michigan where no proper tools could be obtained by the inventor. . . . I am

satisfied, from my knowledge of the printing business, as well as from the operation of the rough machine, with which I am now printing, that the typographer will be ranked with the most novel, useful and pleasing inventions of this age.

And on the reverse side of the same sheet, probably feeling lucky to be allowed any space at all, Burt added:

I, William A. Burt, being duly sworn, depose and say that I am the inventor of the machine, called by me the TYPOG-RAPHER, and intended for use in families, offices and stores, and further that such invention and any parts thereof, have not, to the best of my knowledge and belief, been known or used in the United States or any foreign country.

The inventor made the name of the machine look quite imposing by using solid caps, but he was really not happy about it. It lacked something, he felt. He had written to several papers, including the New York *Commercial Advertiser,* asking for name suggestions and, incidentally, stirring up quite a little interest in the idea of a machine for writing in type. The best suggestion he had received was "Burt's Family Letter Press." He had decided, reluctantly, to stick with "typographer."

President Jackson, along with Secretary of State Martin Van Buren, signed the patent on July 23rd. And Burt, who wanted to be a surveyor more than anything, found himself with the full and exclusive right and liberty of making, constructing, using and vending to others to be used the said machine for printing.

That right and liberty, as scores of later typewriter inventors were to find, was a swift pain in the neck.

Sheldon was bullish. Sheldon could see the population of the entire civilized world punching out neatly printed manuscripts on royalty-paying typographers. Sheldon could see Burt as rich as a pig, and that part of it sounded good to Burt. But all Sheldon's money was in the *Gazette*. Burt not only didn't have any money; his log house wasn't finished, his five sons were eating like five sons, he was hopelessly behind on his paper work, and he felt he ought to be out and around stirring up a mill-construction job or, better, a survey to run. Nevertheless, Burt started working on an improved model, something a little better-looking that might catch a capitalist's eye. It took more than six months to finish the second model, but when she was done she was beautiful, a thing the size and shape of a modest pinball-game machine with four gracious, tapered, Hepplewhite-style legs, and including several mechanical improvements.

There were no typographer backers around Detroit, however, just as there were only poor facilities for making writing machines. Burt went to New York looking for capital and to get some parts properly machined. Sheldon followed. On March 13, 1830, Burt wrote a letter to his wife Phoebe. It has often been quoted as the "first typewritten letter," which of course it was not. It was not even the first typographed letter. Not to mention the hundreds of missives that may have been written on those foreigners' machines. It was just a routine note containing several typographical errors:

> My Dear Companion—
>
> This is the first specimen I send you except a few lines i printed to regulate the machine. I am in good health. . . . Mr. Sheldon arrived here four days ago he went immediately on to Washington and took my moddle for the Patent Office, he will return here next week at which time I shall put my machine on sale and shall sell out the patent as soon as I can and return home. . . .

The story would seem a little sad at this point, since there was no one who wanted to buy the rights to the typographer and Burt and Sheldon had to come home after a complete defeat that had cost a lot in out-of-pocket expenses alone.

Burt had wasted much more time and money than he could afford, and nothing ever came of his writing machine, but feeling sorry for him would be quite inappropriate. He shrugged the whole thing off after he got home, and started working on another invention which interested him more: a compass for surveying that used the sun to establish direction instead of the earth's magnetic attraction. It was patented in 1836 and 1840. For the next seventy-five years it was *the* surveyor's compass, standard equipment for every United States Government survey crew. Better still, Burt found quite a few surveying jobs. In 1831, he was appointed Macomb County Surveyor. In 1833 he was made United States Deputy Surveyor, *and* associate justice of the county court, *and* postmaster of Mount Vernon. He was finally able to drop the annoying flour-mill- and sawmill-building business completely, and spend all his time, very nearly, running surveys to his heart's content. He made the official government survey of Michigan's pleasant peninsula, and of big hunks of Iowa. A dispute blew up over where Michigan ended and Wisconsin began; Judge Burt resurveyed the line, and that was the end of that. He taught all five of his sons how to survey, as well as scores of other young men from far and wide.

In 1844 the Judge was busily surveying with his crew on the Upper Peninsula, near Teal Lake, using not his own solar compass but a magnetic one. Its needle began to jump around like crazy.

"Boys, look around and see what you can find," Burt said.

What the boys found was outcroppings of iron ore. It looked like quite a good deal. It was, of course, part of one of the world's richest deposits. The boys were as excited as if they had stumbled on gold. Judge Burt was excited, too, but for a different reason. He'd gotten out his solar compass to prove that, where the foolish magnetic compass showed deviations up to eighty-seven degrees, the solar compass worked just as well as ever.

Burt was among the first to see that a canal to connect Lake Superior with Lake Huron, by-passing St. Mary's Falls, would be a good thing. He served in the Michigan legislature in 1852–53, and, as chairman of the Committee on Internal Improve-

In 1853 the Handwriting Speed Record was 30 Words a Minute

ments, he pushed hard for the idea. Michigan began to build the Soo Canal, with federal aid, in 1853. In 1856, Burt patented a third invention. It may have meant more to him than the typographer and the solar compass put together, for it was an equatorial sextant. The United States Navy used it. Burt died of a heart attack, two years later, while he was teaching a class of twelve veteran Great Lakes captains the astronomy they needed to understand to navigate with Burt's sextant. Which was not bad for a boy who, lacking a text, had deduced his astronomy from secondary sources.

After Burt's typographer had been patented, the typewriter idea began popping out all over. Some inventors were inspired by the typographer's failure. Many more worked entirely independently without realizing that someone else had already thought of a writing machine; they were driven by that fascinating imperative that sets like-minded men in widely separated places thinking along similar lines at about the same time without the exchange of communications.

There were good reasons for men to invent typewriters.

Burt had been goaded into action by one of the more valid ones: the pen was annoyingly slow. An expert penman, trying his best, might be able to write at a rate of thirty words per minute, but most writers were something less than expert. The tedium was bad enough in itself, but after 1840, when Samuel F. B. Morse patented his electric telegraph, it seemed worse. In short order a whole generation of telegraphers had appeared who could understand code a lot faster than they could write it down. Shorthand stenographers were in a similar fix. They could take their notes as quickly as a man could speak, and yet they couldn't transcribe faster than at a snail's pace.

Not to mention the fact that handwriting was hard to read, and showed no signs of getting better.

The materials for typewriter inventing were widely dis-

Charles Thurber's Printing Machine, 1843

tributed: cast type, available in assorted sizes at print shops
everywhere; clockwork; brass, copper and machine tools; pianos,
each of which embodied the notion that a key, firmly pushed
down, could activate a hammer and deliver a forceful, rapid
blow. The ingredients almost called out for some ingenious
fellow to put them together. The conviction was widely held
that with a few odd bits and pieces, some thought and time
for tinkering, man could work out a gadget to perform almost
any function man could think up.

Typewriter inventions came thick and fast. In 1833, a printer
in Marseilles, France, patented a "Ktypographic" machine. His
name was Xavier Projean: His invention had type bars arranged
in a semicircle that struck down towards the printing point,
which was very promising. But the paper stood still while the

mechanism moved, which was clumsy. In 1838, M. Dujardin of Lille, France, invented a typewriter that looked just like a piano, and in 1840 Jaan Jaackson, the Russian, invented a typewriter that looked like a permanent-wave machine. That same year, two Englishmen, Alexander Bain and Thomas Wright, who later invented a telegraphic printer, patented a writing machine that was to be used, specifically, by electric-telegraph operators. Charles Thurber of Worcester, Massachusetts, invented two different typewriters, one in 1843 and the other in 1845. Neither worked too well, but together they incorporated several important typewriter ideas, such as the notion of a

John H. Cooper's 1856 Machine

Dr. Samuel W. Francis Patented his Literary Piano in 1857

cylindrical roller, or platen, to hold the paper, which would move from right to left for the letter spacing and rotate to make the lines.

And still they came. There were ten more typewriter inventions—seven in France, two in the United States and one in Italy—before 1850, when Oliver T. Eddy of Baltimore, Maryland, invented a magnificent machine, with seventy-eight type bars in thirteen rows, as complicated and about as big as a baby grand. At almost the same time, J. B. Fairbanks invented his "phonetic writer," which was intended to print on calico as well as paper.

In 1852, John M. Jones of Clyde, New York, invented a typewriter that did exceptionally good, but slow, work. He called it the "mechanical typographer," which seemed to encroach on

John Jones Circulated This Flyer to Publicize His "Typographer," 1852

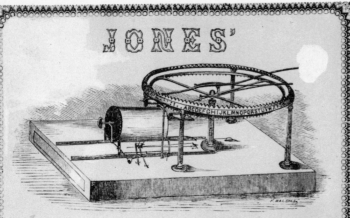

TYPOGRAPHER.

PATENTED JUNE 1, 1852.

FOR PRINTING

Letters, Poetry, Cards, Extracts, Lessons, Compositions,

Notes, &c., as fast as the majority of People can write with a Pen,

WITHOUT SETTING UP THE TYPE!

For Families and Schools it meets with universal favor, as by its use young people and children will learn composition, punctuation and spelling; and it is also a source of much amusement.

For printing the important documents of the Lawyer, the prescriptions of the Doctor, and may be advantageously used in nearly every business office.

For the Sermons, Notes, Heads, &c. of the Preacher and public speaker.

It may be advantageously used in localities remote from Printing Offices, for printing advertisements, handbills, circulars, cards, &c. It is also adapted to the wants of the blind.

It is easily managed, and any child that can read, will, with a few hours practice, print accurately.

In the **Scientific American** of March 6th, 1852, the following language is used in relation to this **Press:**—" It is, in truth, a most valuable invention ; we have seen his model, and feel proud and pleased with it. It can print a letter faster than the majority of people can write one with a pen, and we wish one was in every family."

State, County or Town rights, (except the **New England States, Ohio, Indiana** and **Louisiana,** which are sold,) may be purchased at moderate rates. Address

JOHN JONES & Co.,

CLYDE, Wayne Co., N. Y.

Steam Press of G. M. Davison, Saratoga Springs.

Burt's nomenclature. In 1854, R. S. Thomas of Wilmington, North Carolina, invented a "typograph," giving the odd word almost generic status. There were two more in 1856: John Cooper of Philadelphia patented a big, rugged machine, notable for its paper-feed mechanism, and Alfred E. Beach, for years the editor of *Scientific American,* patented a writing machine, later billed in his magazine as "the original type writer." In 1857, Dr. Samuel W. Francis of New York patented a writing machine that had the size, shape and general appearance of a piano accordion.

The pace quickened. Between October, 1857, when Dr. Francis got his patent, and June, 1868, when Christopher Sholes, Carlos Glidden and S. W. Soule got theirs, thirteen more typewriters were invented, eight of them by Americans, including F. A. de May of New York, Benjamin Livermore of Hartford, Vermont, George House of Buffalo, New York, Abner Peeler of Webster City, Iowa, John Pratt of Centre, Alabama, and Thomas Hall of Brooklyn, New York. Livermore's machine was the most interesting of the lot. He concocted a special alphabet of character signs, made up of only about half a dozen straight lines, so that only half a dozen keys were necessary. The operator superimposed one impression on top of another, and built up

Thomas Hall's "Typographic Machine," 1867

the letters for himself. A great idea, although it never caught on, perhaps because the result looked as much like Greek as English. Pratt's was the most important writing machine in this group. He called it the "pterotype." His patent was granted in England, and a London magazine, *Engineering*, printed a descriptive article which Beach picked up and reprinted in the *Scientific American*. The important thing about Pratt's typewriter was the fact that Christopher Sholes read the reprinted article.

4 / By Jingo! It Prints

The fifty-second man to invent the typewriter was Christopher Latham Sholes of Milwaukee.

Most encyclopedias refer to him as the typewriter's "father," which is fitting enough despite the crowd that was there ahead of him. Sholes's was the first practical commercial machine.

His half a hundred predecessors had produced some ingenious notions, but their models possessed a common fault: they were as slow, or slower, than writing with a pen. Nearly all of them did neat, legible work. But before the typewriter could interest buyers it needed to be faster. Pens of standard quality were selling for one cent and a dime would buy a lot of ink. Something in the neighborhood of $100 for a typewriter seemed too much unless the buyer could be promised a rebate in the form of saved time.

Sholes was forty-eight years old and a man with a long, fairly distinguished career behind him as a newspaperman, printer and politician when he read a magazine article about Pratt's experiments with the "pterotype." He had edited the Wisconsin

Inquirer, the Southport (afterwards Kenosha) *Telegraph,* and the Milwaukee *Daily Sentinel and News.* He had served in the Wisconsin legislature, been Milwaukee's postmaster, and was, at the time in question, the summer of 1867, the Collector of Customs. He looked more like a poet than any of the things he was or had been. His eyes were sad, like a poet's. He was tall, slender to the point of frailty, with long flowing hair, a short beard, and a medium-length mustache, and he loved poetry although he didn't write it. He also loved puns. His idea of the world's best joke was a poetic pun. He came home one night, for example, and found that the kerosene lamp in the hall had dripped onto the rug in the hall. According to an eyewitness, Sholes's comment, from Byron's *Don Juan,* was: "The isles of Greece, the isles of grease! Where burning Sappho loved and sung . . ."

Sholes and half a dozen friends spent their spare time inventing things, in the manner of men who are fond of working with their hands; they were tinkerers whose hobby was carpentry and shop work, and their unofficial headquarters was a professional, *bona fide* machine shop, run by C. F. Kleinsteuber in a small frame building on the north edge of Milwaukee. The projects in progress that summer seemed fairly nutty. One fellow, Dr. Henry W. Roby, a court reporter, was fooling around with a trick clock to be used in a magic act. Another, Carlos Glidden, had an idea for a spading machine which, he figured, ought to replace the plow. Sholes, helped by S. W. Soule, a professional machinist, was trying to concoct a gadget to number book pages serially and automatically.

Like most hobbyists, the gang at Kleinsteuber's spent a lot of time talking instead of working. One day Sholes told the boys about the piece he'd read in *Scientific American* describing John Pratt's attempts to perfect a writing machine, and about other, earlier, unsuccessful efforts. Glidden pointed out to Sholes that his paging device, which was fairly well along toward completion, was something of a writing machine. "Why can't you make one that will print words as well as figures?" Glidden asked. "I can," Sholes said. "I've thought about it a great deal, and I'm going to try it."

About a week later, during a night when a bad cough kept him awake, Sholes thought of something: one might cut the type face on the side of a short bar, and make it strike up against a piece of paper held underneath a round glass disc, in approximately the manner of a pianoforte's hammer striking from below against the strings. He told Dr. Roby about it the next day. It sounded good to Roby, who immediately started to whittle one of the requisite parts out of a piece of wood. Sholes told Glidden. Glidden liked the idea and said he wanted to help. Soule thought it could be done. Matthias Schwalbach, one of Kleinsteuber's employees and an expert pattern maker, didn't see why they shouldn't try it.

The first model was not a complete writing machine. It was only the letter "W" and its activating mechanism, a telegraph key linked to a type bar pivoted to hit, from below, against a round glass disc. It was finished in July, at some expense to the magic clock, the serial pager and the spading machine, which were temporarily sidetracked. Sholes borrowed a sheet of carbon paper from a friend in the Western Union office, the only place in Milwaukee that had one. The friend, Charles E. Weller, naturally wanted to know what Sholes planned to do with it. Sholes wouldn't say. But he did invite Weller to come around the next day to his office in the Federal Building, about noon, "to see something interesting."

Weller appeared as per invitation. He found Sholes and Glidden, their fingers smudged, playing with the odd little device. The carbon paper was used as a substitute for ink. Sholes held a thin sheet of paper and the carbon with his left hand against

*Christopher L. Sholes, Whose Typewriter Was the First to be
Manufactured and Marketed*

the underside of the glass. Then, as he drew them slowly from
right to left, he tapped the telegraph key with his right hand.
He handed Weller the result:

W W W W W W W W W W W W W W W W W W W W W

It was quite a journey from there to a machine that would

write not only "W" but the entire alphabet, punctuation marks, and the numerals from 2 to 9. Sholes had the general plan in mind, however, and by September he finished a complete working model, with handsome black walnut, piano-style keys lettered in white. He was the host at a small party at Kleinsteuber's to celebrate. In addition to his fellow hobbyists, and the shop's professional personnel, there was a newspaper reporter in the group. Sholes sat down at the machine and, with his eye cocked toward posterity, wrote: "C. LATHAM SHOLES, SEPT. 1867." It was in solid caps for the good and sufficient reason that the machine had no lower-case characters.

The reporter was impressed, although apparently he didn't try the writing machine himself, for he wrote in longhand:

They let the funny thing go,
And by jingo!
It prints the lingo
Of a red flamingo,
A Greek or gringo,
A monk or mingo,
Great Dane or dingo.

It was an exciting occasion, but all hands agreed that the model could stand some improvement. Disassembly began almost immediately. Sholes had learned a lot in the process of building the first model and he knew he could do better. He did not know that he would be making one writing machine after another, practically without interruption, during the next six years, or that, at the end of the time, it would still be full of bugs.

One thing—and practically only one thing—was set. Sholes had a name for the machine, which had been called, up to halfway through the first model, "the machine." All the Kleinsteuber group had tried to think of something more distinctive. They had tried "writing machine" and "printing machine," but neither

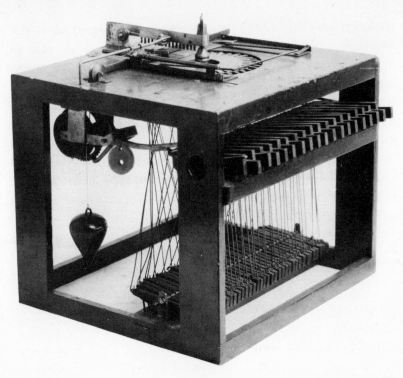

The Improved Second Version of the Sholes-Glidden-Soule (1868)

one made it entirely clear what the contraption did. Sholes thought of "type-writer" with a hyphen. Someone objected to "type-writer" on the grounds that that didn't mean anything at all. But there was *something* about "type-writer"; it was provocative, if not clear. Once you knew what a "type-writer" was, it seemed entirely apt. By September "Type-Writer" was its name.

Money loomed far larger, as an obstacle, than mechanical problems. Building patent models was going to be expensive. Kleinsteuber and his workmen, sympathetic and interested though they were, had to be paid for their labors. And manufacture, which was the goal, would take not only cash but capital.

The second model was something less than perfect, but before Sholes took it apart he began to write letters to people offering to let them in on the ground floor in return for ready funds. He wrote to James Densmore of Meadville, Pennsylvania, among a great many others. It was a long shot. Sholes had met Densmore, a lawyer, promoter, salesman and inventor, in Madison some twenty-three years earlier, and had taken an instant dislike to him, or so he later claimed. Densmore had been a newspaperman and job printer at the time, a great, beefy giant with a shaggy red beard and a piercing, almost hypnotic, eye, who made a lot of noise and threw his considerable weight around at every opportunity. Sholes barely knew him, by choice, but he had heard that Densmore had made a killing in the Pennsylvania oil boom by inventing and patenting the first oil tank car. So he addressed a letter, neatly typed.

Sholes was delighted to receive a prompt reply from Densmore saying that he was very much interested, and wanted a part in the writing-machine project. The terms, as finally arranged, were that Densmore was to pay the group's back bills, a matter of $600, and to provide all the future financing, in return for a 25 per cent interest in the rights.

Densmore immediately sealed the agreement, in an impressive fashion, by delivering the $600. Sholes didn't realize that $600 was Densmore's total liquid assets; like many another promoter, Densmore was as skillful at concealing what he was worth as he was at hiding the precise nature of his activities. Whether he was loaded or flat broke, he looked terrible. He affected seedy, battered hats, a long, shabby coat and off-color vests. His trousers were inches too short, and he wore thick wool socks in low-cut shoes. It is possible that Densmore planned his outrageous costume deliberately on the theory that it doesn't matter how a promoter looks just so long as he is noticed and remembered. In view of Densmore's occasional periods of economic distress, the idea of feigning an impoverished, or hobo, look when he had lots of money would have been a masterful stratagem.

Almost all the participants in the project who wrote about it later ripped Densmore to ribbons because, in the end, he captured the rights and royalties, like the traditional villain-exploiter who snatches everything away from the impractical inventor-genius. There is certainly a basis for their spleen. But without Densmore, or somebody like Densmore, the Type-Writer might have come to nothing. In addition to money, he supplied tremendous optimism. He put his money into the machine before he had even seen it. He was its loudest, most fervent champion even after he had seen it. Later, he was hopeful, or appeared to be hopeful, in the darkest hours when everyone else, including Sholes, was ready to give up.

Densmore, shouting and thrashing about, insisted, from '67 to '73, that the Type-Writer was too crude to sell, and he forced Sholes to try one thing after another through nearly fifty different models. Densmore turned the experimental machines over to professional stenographers like Roby and Weller with instructions to give them the toughest practical tests they could devise. They found plenty of faults. The type bars tended to stick and bunch. The weight on the clockwork device that moved the carriage was too light, and the string that held it was liable to break, to the jeopardy of the operator's toes. The thing stuttered and jumped. The hand-inked ribbon was a mess. And yet, despite all troubles, when everything was just right, the Type-Writer could march along at an impressive clip, writing neatly and quickly, especially on a memorized test sentence like the then current political slogan, suggesting that Republicans had better forget their internal squabbles to concentrate on helping Ulysses S. Grant beat Horatio Seymour, "Now is the time for all good men to come to the aid of their party."

On July 30, 1870, Sholes wrote to his friend Weller about the latest version of the Type-Writer:

> . . . I think the machine is now as perfect in its mechanism as I know how to make it, or to have it made. . . . The machine is done, and I want some more worlds to conquer. Life will be most flat, stale and unprofitable without something to invent.

That was Sholes's opinion, not Densmore's.

Five months later, and doubtless to his dismay, Sholes was working an average of sixteen hours a day on a radically improved new model.

Neither Kleinsteuber's nor any of the several other shops where Sholes labored was properly equipped to do Type-Writer work. As Weller said, it was like trying to make a watch in a blacksmith's shop. There was not enough money for dies or adequate machinery, yet the group tried to achieve something like production, first in a battered old stone building beside a canal in West Milwaukee and then in rented premises in Chicago, where fifteen Type-Writers, all the same design, were actually turned out. Unhappily the Chicago landlord wanted his money before the machines were sold, and the manufacturers were forced back to Milwaukee.

It was tough. All the money the group could raise was spent before it had been received. Few Type-Writers were on sale because most of those produced had either been given away for publicity purposes, or were undergoing tests and trials, or were held by creditors; but the few more than filled the demand. Everyone felt and looked discouraged except Densmore, who either did not know the meaning of despair, or was an actor of consummate skill; or some of both. Densmore charged about the countryside demanding an improved Type-Writer, and writing glibly to the boys about large, rosy deals he could see on the horizon. The expenses of maintaining a bold front were

A Young Lady at Work with a Sholes-Glidden-Soule Type-writer in 1872

so heavy that Densmore, for a time, was forced to live on raw apples and soda crackers eaten secretly in his various hotel rooms. Yet not a single eyewitness, out of the many who disliked him, recalled a moment when Densmore's faith in the Type-Writer and in his ability to make a killing out of it wavered for as much as a fraction of a second.

At one point Densmore wired Sholes from New York that he had a big deal with Western Union under way and that he needed Sholes, in person, to help swing it. Not long afterwards

Densmore and Sholes called on the president of the company, with the frail Sholes carrying the Type-Writer and Densmore leading the way, to give a demonstration. Western Union seemed interested, but wanted time to let some of its telegraphers have a look at the machine.

Weeks went by. Sholes was sure that the telegraphers had turned their thumbs down. Densmore was positive that they'd loved the Type-Writer, and couldn't do without it. Sholes was afraid that the price Densmore had asked, $50,000 for the exclusive manufacturing rights, had ruined everything.

No word came. Finally Densmore, unable to stand the suspense, went back and asked. Western Union's explanation was painful: they liked it a lot, but one of their employees, a Thomas A. Edison by name, thought he could put together something better for a lot less than $50,000. And Western Union had decided to wait to see what Edison might figure out.

(What Edison figured out, eventually, was good but not a typewriter. It was an electric printing wheel, patented in 1872, a forerunner of the stock market tape ticker.)

"I believe in the invention from the topmost corner of my hat to the bottom-most head of the nails of my boot heels," Densmore roared at about this time. He was either telling the exact truth or hurling defiance at his miserable fortune.

Densmore's share in the rights, originally a mere 25 per cent, was gradually increasing. At each crisis—and crisis was almost the normal state of the project—Densmore howled with pain. Money was needed for additional patent models on each improvement. Money was needed to pay the most urgent bills. Densmore argued that he had to get something for raising it. There was only one way he could be paid: by increasing his percentage interest in the invention.

The original shareholders, since profits appeared completely improbable, turned their theoretical pieces over to Densmore, one percentage here and another there, until, by 1872, Glidden,

Soule, Roby and Schwalbach had nothing left. Sholes still owned some rights. A new participant, George Washington Yost, was involved because Densmore had sold him part of his own interest. Together, Yost and Densmore talked Sholes into selling his rights for a flat fee. The price is disputed. It may have been anything from $1,200 to $40,000, but it was probably around $6,000, and payable in installments. In any case, it was absurdly little.

Yost, in the opinion of some of his colleagues, was the smoothest talker ever born. He had been a poor New York State farm boy but he talked so well and so fast that many persons mistook him for a man of social distinction, probably independently wealthy, who busied himself with all sorts of inventions and promotions just to escape boredom. Like Densmore, Yost was a soldier of fortune. Physically, and in style, however, he was everything Densmore was not. Densmore, the bull in the china shop, infuriated many of those who had anything to do with him. Yost, by contrast, was all diplomacy; suave, magnetic and well liked. He exuded the faint, delicious aroma of gilt-edged investments, and it was embarrassing for creditors to press him too hard for payments because he seemed so far above a sordid matter like money. Yet, like Densmore, he had been raised, financially speaking, in the midst of the dirty infighting over Pennsylvania oil. He was also an inventor. He had invented a leak-proof oil barrel which might have made him a fortune if Densmore had not invented the tank car which rendered the barrel partly obsolete. He had invented a reaping and sewing machine and was manufacturing it at Corry, Pennsylvania. He had a fairly large factory, and looked like the very model of a prosperous minor manufacturer. And yet, when Densmore talked about his half-baked Type-Writer proposition Yost was ready to sell the farm-equipment business, which he did, to raise money to go into the writing-machine speculation.

The 1873 Sholes-Glidden-Soule machine, which Densmore

Sholes's Daughter Contemplating the 1872 Model

and Yost owned, bore only faint resemblance to the first experimental model. What had begun by looking like a large, complicated mousetrap now appeared to be a typewriter. It had a four-bank keyboard with the letters and characters arranged very nearly in what has ever since been called "standard" order. The machine was partially encased in a japanned tin case, squarish and rather tall. The carriage was a dinky affair, with a short, fat roller. But it was a carriage, and it ran back and forth horizontally as carriages do today, although it was still motivated by the weight of a saucy leaden ball on a string that dangled down on the right-hand end of the machine. The biggest difference between the 1873 concept and modern typewriters was the under-strike idea; as in the first model, the type bars hit upwards against the bottom of the roller or platen. The printing point was therefore out of sight, and the operator could not see what had been written, or whether the thing was working properly, until three or four lines after the fact.

Densmore and Yost, like almost everybody with an invention that needs selling and publicizing, spent some time in Washington, D.C., hoping to persuade the government, or a department, or a part of a department, to adopt the Type-Writer as official equipment. Quite a few bureaucrats were friendly, and some spoke in a complimentary manner about the machine, but adoption was out of the question. Every agency was bound by miles of red tape prescribing in excruciating detail what records were to be kept and how they were to be kept. Such procedural orders couldn't be changed except on the highest level. And nowhere was there a word about *typewritten* matter. Densmore was outraged. He was positive that eventually government offices would bristle with tens of thousands of Type-Writers and furious that the day had to be postponed.

Next they tried talking to Philo Remington, the eldest of Eliphalet Remington's three sons, and president of the family business, which was making guns, sewing machines and farm machinery. The Remingtons had a wonderful factory at Ilion, New York, equipped with more punches, drills and machine tools than C. F. Kleinsteuber had ever dreamed about, and more capacity than they were using because after the Civil War boom things had been on the slow side, at least comparatively speaking.

Densmore and Yost took a room at Small's Hotel, later called the Osgood House, set up the Type-Writer, and demonstrated it to Philo Remington and several others. Yost did almost all the talking. He had never been more eloquent.

A contract was signed on March 1, 1873. Remington agreed to set apart an entire wing of the plant for Type-Writer production, and to manufacture one thousand of the machines. Densmore and Yost were to be the selling agents for the product, and it was to bear the famous Remington name.

A month later the work was in progress. Remington put two great mechanics on the job, William K. Jenne, who had been head of the sewing-machine division, and Jefferson M. Clough, a wizard at the infinitely difficult task of remodeling the machine to make it suitable for quantity production. In very short order, Jenne and Clough had solved dozens of the problems that had haunted Sholes, Glidden, Roby, Schwalbach, Soule, Weller and the others. Actual manufacture began in September. The first shipments were made early in 1874.

There is an old joke about the Maine fisherman who painted pictures of boats. He was asked to paint a portrait. He didn't care much for the idea. But the prospective sitter insisted. Finally the fisherman agreed, reluctantly, to try a portrait. "But don't be surprised," he warned, "if you come out looking a lot like a boat."

Jenne was a sewing-machine man. He had been a sewing-machine man for years. He liked sewing machines. So the first

Remington Type-Writer naturally looked a lot like a sewing machine, with a foot-treadle carriage return of sewing-machine design and gay flowers stenciled on its black metal front and sides.

5 / The 1881 Revolution

The men who had managed, after epic labors, to get into production with a practical modification of the Sholes-Glidden-Soule were compelled to face a hideous reality: practically no one was interested in paying $125 for a Type-Writer. The first Remingtons were shipped from Ilion early in the year. Almost immediately some were shipped right back for further adjustment, because they weren't working as well as they should. That in itself was disheartening, but sales agents Densmore and Yost, along with the Western Electric Company, which had agreed to handle distribution in some of the western sales territories, had to cope with a more distressing problem: many Remingtons were gathering dust on dealers' shelves. A dissatisfied customer is a bother, but no customer at all is a disaster.

The public at large, never having heard of the Type-Writer, was apathetic. Individuals, when the machine had been brought to their attention, usually thought it was outrageously expensive. Luckily there were exceptions. Mark Twain was among the most notable. He fell for the typewriter idea only a few months after the first Remington went on sale, and when he fell

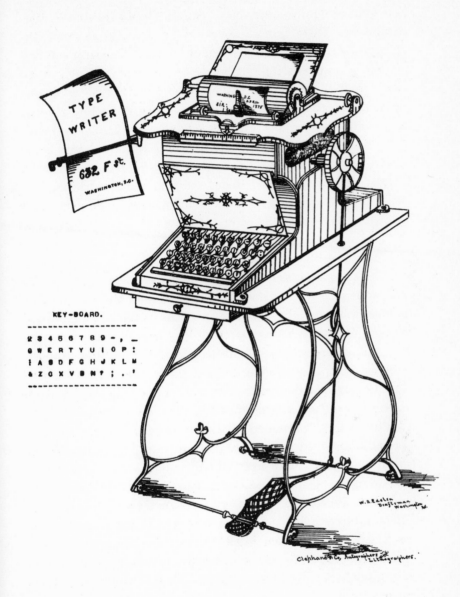

The Typewriter that Mark Twain Bought

he fell hard. He became the first of the typewriter buffs, that curious breed which really loves the device with an unreasonable passion, something above and beyond mere appreciation of utility, and therefore feels free to complain about it with abandon. The meeting between Twain, whose real name was Clemens, and his first typewriter took place in Boston. He was on a lecture tour, and was taking a window-shopping stroll with the humorist, Petroleum V. Nasby, whose real name was D. R. Locke, when they saw a Remington Model 1 on display inside a store. They went right in to find out what in the world it could be. A salesman showed them the machine, explained its general principles, and made the claim that it could write at a speed of fifty-seven words a minute.

Twain said he didn't believe it could.

The salesman called out a young lady to demonstrate the Type-Writer. Nasby and Twain timed her with their own watches. She ripped off fifty-seven words in almost exactly sixty seconds. It was luck, Twain insisted; he was confident that the girl couldn't repeat the astonishing feat. The girl did it again.

Nasby and Twain were delighted. They stayed for a long time, begging the demonstrator to repeat the performance again and again, and apparently they regarded her acquiescence as a tribute to their combined charms, not entirely realizing that she was employed for exactly that purpose. The girl wrote the speed samples on short sheets of paper, and as fast as she turned them out, Nasby and Twain took them and stuffed them in their pockets, thinking that they were fine souvenirs. Before the end of the afternoon, Twain's sales resistance, such as it was, had vanished. He put down his $125 and bought a Type-Writer, to be delivered to his home in Hartford, Connecticut.

Not until they got back to their hotel and examined the type-written specimens stuffing their pockets did Twain understand how he and Nasby had been tricked. Twain says, in his autobiography:

We got out our slips and were a little disappointed to find that they all contained the same words. The girl had economized time and labor by memorizing a formula which she knew by heart.

At home I played with the toy, repeating and repeating and repeating "The boy stood on the burning deck" until I could turn out that boy's adventure at the rate of twelve words a minute; then I resumed the pen for business, and only worked the machine to astonish inquisitive visitors. They carried off reams of the boy and his burning deck.

That was the tone he took long after the event, however. The moment he got back to Hartford, disappointment or no, he sat right down and began to play with the machine. He wrote this letter on December 9, 1874, to his brother, Orion Clemens:

DEAR BROTHER:

I AM TRYING TO GET THE HANG OF THIS NEW FANGLED WRITING MACHINE, BUT I AM NOT MAKING A SHINING SUCCESS OF IT. HOWEVER THIS IS THE FIRST ATTEMPT I HAVE EVER MADE & YET I PERCEIVE I SHALL SOON & EASILY ACQUIRE A FINE FACILITY IN ITS USE.... THE MACHINE HAS SEVERAL VIRTUES. I BELIEVE IT WILL PRINT FASTER THAN I CAN WRITE. ONE MAY LEAN BACK IN HIS CHAIR & WORK IT. IT PILES AN AWFUL STACK OF WORDS ON ONE PAGE. IT DON'T MUSS THINGS OR SCATTER INK BLOTS AROUND. OF COURSE IT SAVES PAPER. . . . WORKING THE TYPE-WRITER REMINDS ME OF OLD ROBERT BUCHANAN, WHO, YOU REMEMBER, USED TO SET UP ARTICLES AT THE CASE WITHOUT PREVIOUSLY PUTTING THEM IN THE FORM OF MANUSCRIPT. I WAS LOST IN ADMIRATION OF SUCH MARVELOUS INTELLECTUAL CAPACITY. . . .

YOUR BROTHER,

SAM

Three months later, in March, 1875, Twain wrote a testimonial for Remington. It was perhaps not exactly what the editor of the advertising catalogue wanted. He had the good sense, none the less, to include it among more flowery tributes from Type-Writer users:

> Gentlemen: Please do not use my name in any way. Please do not even divulge the fact that I own a machine. I have entirely stopped using the Type-Writer, for the reason that I never could write a letter with it to anybody without receiving a request by return mail that I would not only describe the machine but state what progress I had made in the use of it, etc., etc. I don't like to write letters, and so I don't want people to know that I own this curiosity breeding little joker.
>
> Yours truly,
Saml L. Clemens.

Tom Sawyer appeared in 1876 and, according to Twain's autobiography, the manuscript was typed before it was submitted to a publisher. The Herkimer County (New York) Historical Society, however, believes that Twain made a slip; that he confused *Tom Sawyer* with *Life on the Mississippi* (1883). In any case, Twain was the first author in history to turn in a typewritten book manuscript, starting a double-spaced, one-side-of-the-page trend that has pleased editors ever since.

The fact that Nasby failed to buy a Type-Writer that same fateful afternoon should not be taken as a reflection on the demonstrator's persuasiveness. On the contrary, Nasby was so impressed by what he'd seen that he promptly gave up the lecture racket and started selling Type-Writers himself. He became a partner in the sales organization, and the name of the firm, for a time, was Densmore, Yost & Locke.

Yet for every Mark Twain and every Petroleum Nasby, there were tens of thousands of good citizens, most of whom traveled under their real names, who were able to resist Type-Writer

Remington Typewriter Shown at the Centennial Exhibition, Philadelphia, 1876

demonstrations almost completely. Remington had an exhibit, for instance, at the Centennial Exposition at Philadelphia in 1876. There was a pretty girl with a Type-Writer, and, for 25 cents, she would write out a brief note suitable for mailing to the folks back home. Remington salesmen everywhere figured to profit by the gimmick, which was calculated not only to impress Exposition visitors but to fill the United States mails with advertising material that had been stamped and paid for by

potential customers. The exhibit drew well. There were lines of
people waiting to dictate notes, most of whom seemed fascinated by the machine and the girl's dexterity. The tragedy was
that the public was indifferent to the idea that, for a consideration, any man could buy one of the intriguing machines for his
very own. All anyone seemed to want was one, or perhaps two,
of the 25-cent samples of the Type-Writer's work. Remington
sales continued as slow as ever, both in Philadelphia and in
the outlying postal zones.

The exposition was a disappointment to Sholes, too, who was
there in person and rather expecting a fuss to be made over him
as the inventor—or, at least, the principal inventor—of the
mechanical age's latest marvel. Another inventor got just the
sort of reception Sholes had in mind: speeches, medals, prize
awards and all the trimmings. His name was Alexander Graham
Bell. He was exhibiting, for the first time in public, a silly-
looking affair called the "telephone," which was not even on
the market.

The Remington sales picture brightened ever so slightly in
1877 when the Ithaca, New York, sales agent, a fellow named
William O. Wyckoff, started to publish a thin periodical called
The Typewriter Magazine. That journal, according to its mast-
head, was "devoted to true reform, to the welfare of all mankind, and to advancement and improvement in all things." One
particular reform interested Wyckoff to the virtual exclusion of
all others: he wanted mankind to swear off pen and ink and
take to typewriting. Despite its somewhat monomaniac devotion
to this single subject, *The Typewriter Magazine* had unde-
niable appeal. Wyckoff used one device that is common now-
adays among science-fiction writers. He wrote about improbable

---

"The Typewriter is Now Perfected." From Wyckoff's Magazine,
1878

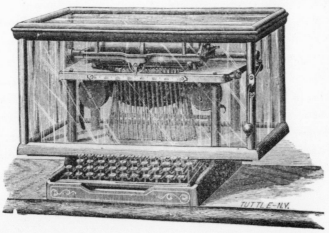

future events in the past tense. He spoke as if every educated person of any account was using the Type-Writer, and had been for a considerable period of time, and he threw in all kinds of small details to lend verisimilitude to what was, in fact, no more than one Remington salesman's dream. In an editorial in his January, 1878, issue, for instance, Wyckoff casually announced that: "We are happy to inform . . . the public generally that the typewriter is now perfected." What had actually happened was that Remington had introduced its second model, which it called Model 4. According to *The Typewriter Magazine*, there was no longer any achievement left for the typewriter industry, because Model 4 was everything the machine could ever be Wyckoff admitted, for the first time, that some persons had held off on the old model because they wanted to wait for a better one. But now, he argued, was the time to buy. The new machine, among other things, was both "noiseless" and "portable;" that is to say, as extra equipment, one could buy a large square glass box, like an inverted fish tank, which fitted over everything except the keys and cut down on the clatter; and, since the sewing-machine treadle had been abandoned, and the new machine weighed not more than twenty-five pounds, any strong-backed young man ought to be able to pick it up.

Wyckoff's prose, and even his arithmetic, had a sanguine quality. On the question of speed-economy, he figured out that, since the typewriter could go as fast as seventy-five words a minute compared to the pen's turtlelike twenty-four wpm, a "good operator" could do "from three to twenty hours' work in one hour." How he got that "twenty" remains a mystery, although, in all fairness, he did not specifically say what kind of work the operator might have in mind. On public health, Wyckoff declared that the Type-Writer offered "a complete safeguard" for editors, authors and all others whose time was largely spent in writing against "pen paralysis, loss of sight, and curvature of the spine."

One *Typewriter Magazine* article was on the subject of How To Get Rich Quick. The solution was easy: "Purchase a Type-Writer and, having become expert, obtain a situation in some Law, Insurance, Manufacturing or Merchant's office as a corresponding clerk or copyist. An operator with a machine will have no trouble in procuring a situation at a good salary." For the sake of complete candor, the piece might have added that good salaries for corresponding clerks or copyists, at the time, ranged from $7 to $15 a week, so that if some poor beggar had taken the advice, and had managed to amortize his $125 investment at, say, 50 cents a week, it would have taken him from 1878 to 1883 to pay for the machine.

Testimonials were a regular feature of *The Typewriter Magazine*. For example, Delos L. Holden, a wholesale grocer from Elmira, New York, wrote:

> It gives me pleasure to say that the Type-Writer has been, so far, a source of unalloyed pleasure. I find that I now, after three months experience in its use, write considerably faster with it than with a pen, and certainly with more ease, and without taxing my eyes in the least. . . . I find too that the machine does not get out of order, and will take almost anything from a sheet of Bristol-board to a dog's ear, and print on it. . . . I would no more think of doing without it than of asking my wife to dispense with her sewing machine.

Wyckoff's journalistic efforts were a step in the direction of true reform, but not every dealer was blessed with comparable fire and imagination. Densmore, Yost and Locke were worried. Yost paid a visit to Erastus Fairbanks, inventor of the Fairbanks scales, at St. Johnsbury, Vermont, who was doing a brisk business, with the help of his sons, selling weighing machines. Yost persuaded Fairbanks to take over the sales of writing machines, too. Fairbanks put a twenty-three-year-old, C. W. Seamans, in charge of the Type-Writer division of his sales organization, which was by no means an insult to the Type-Writer, for Seamans had already proven that he was a selling fool. He wore his hair parted in the middle and long over the ears. His face was open and honest. He had deep, soulful eyes and a noble brow, and, looking like a combination poet and revivalist-meeting preacher, Seamans had closed hundreds of scales deals all over New England. Many of Seamans' customers did not realize that they were up against perhaps the most irresistible salesman in the United States until he had left, and they found that they owned an expensive weighing device although they had nothing in particular they wanted to weigh. For all Seamans' ability, however, the job of selling Type-Writers proved too tough for the Fairbanks outfit, and they passed the ball to E. Remington & Sons, which had been, until that year, merely the manufacturer and the name-lender. Remington took Seamans, now all of twenty-seven, away from Fairbanks and kept him in his Type-Writer selling post. Total typewriter sales in 1881 came to twelve hundred machines, and E. Remington & Sons took a dark view of future possibilities.

But Seamans, who could have been as discouraged as anybody, was brightly optimistic. He and the enthusiastic Wyckoff from Ithaca went to have a chat with Henry H. Benedict, a Remington executive and one of those who had believed in the Type-Writer from the day Densmore and Yost had first brought the demonstration model to Ilion. The three optimists, Wyckoff, Seamans and Benedict, formed a new company of that name on August 1, 1882. They bought the Remington Type-Writer sales-agency rights in the United States and in the entire world, for good measure, and they committed themselves to take as

many typewriters as Jenne and his workmen could squeeze out
of the Type-Writer wing of the big factory.

It was a great triumvirate. Wyckoff was big and hearty, with
a grandiose white mustache that formed an inverted V so generous that one could hardly see his mouth at all and projecting
down past both sides of his jutting, cleft chin, for a good half
inch. His style was to overwhelm objections with sheer vitality.
Benedict looked like a Viennese doctor in a yeast advertisement.
He was bald, with a full beard and pince-nez glasses. He wore
towering stand-up collars, and he seemed to epitomize sound,
conservative, sophisticated judgment. He was forbidding and
dignified, the perfect complement to Seamans' air of wistful
innocence, like a fine boy badly in need of someone to mother
him. Wyckoff, Seamans & Benedict opened offices on lower
Broadway in Manhattan. They did so well that in five years
they owned the Remington Type-Writer lock, stock and barrel
including the wing of the Ilion factory, all the patents, all the
franchises and everything else involved in the manufacture and
distribution of the machine. From 1886 on, Remington Type-
Writer and E. Remington & Sons were separate companies.

It took miraculous footwork on the part of Wyckoff, Seamans
& Benedict to go from nowhere to a position of being able to buy
the Type-Writer from Philo Remington. One real difficulty,
among the many that confronted them, was the public's feeling
that typewriting, for private correspondence, was insulting, or
confusing, or both. Handbills could be printed, a good many
persons felt, but letters were written in longhand with pen and
ink. Jenne ran into this assumption on one occasion when he
wrote to a hotel in New York to ask for a reservation. As the
Type-Writer's godfather, he naturally typed his request. When
he got to the desk of the hotel on the specified day, Jenne found,
to his dismay, that he had no room. He protested that he'd

Office of the General Electric Co. in 1882

---

written long in advance. A light dawned in the clerk's face. He'd received Jenne's request, but he hadn't been able to figure out why a guest would go to all the trouble of having an ordinary letter printed, so he had assumed that it was some sort of advertising stunt. The clerk had thrown it into the wastebasket without taking any action of any kind.

Some persons' feelings were hurt by the receipt of a typewritten letter on the grounds that the printing was an aspersion cast on their ability to read longhand. A Texas insurance man, J. P. Johns, one of the early Type-Writer users, sent a typed note to one of his agents and got back an indignant reply: "I do not think it was necessary then, nor will it be in the future, to have your letters to me taken to the printers' and set up like a handbill.

I will be able to read your writing, and I am deeply chagrined to think you thought such a course necessary."

Others regarded the Type-Writer as an invader of privacy, on the theory that no man was clever enough to run such a machine without a professional operator's help, and that therefore a typewritten love letter must have been transcribed by a third person.

Wyckoff, Seamans & Benedict had lots of other resistances to overcome. They went about their work in a systematic, inspired manner, attacking one difficulty after another, but their biggest break was a present, a stroke of luck, handed to them by the Young Women's Christian Association.

The shortage of trained typists was acute. Shorthand stenography was booming, but few persons had realized that shorthand and typing might logically go together; the shorthand reporters were men who were reasonably well paid, and although it had been urged that they purchase Type-Writers, the idea had been that they could dictate from their notes to a typist in order to save transcription time. Not more than one or two schools taught typing, and for a good reason: since the Type-Writer's future seemed highly dubious, and typists were earning, on the average, not more than $10 a week, not many young men were interested.

In 1881 the Central Branch of the YWCA in New York City started to teach eight young ladies to typewrite.

There had been a few girl typists who had acted as demonstrators, but the YWCA had a different idea; it was thinking of typing as a career opportunity for young ladies.

There was criticism. "An obvious error in judgment by well-meaning but misguided ladies," was the opinion of one observer. Another commentator, a man, predicted that the minds and constitutions of the eight student typists would undoubtedly break down completely under the strain of a six months course. All eight were hired within a short period of time to work in business offices where the only previous female employees had been scrubbing women who cleaned up at night. The YWCA got hundreds of requests it couldn't fill. The directors had to send back polite word that, until another class had been graduated, the supply of girls was unfortunately exhausted.

And that was it. The revolution came rather quietly, on high-buttoned shoes, accompanied not by gunfire or bombs bursting in air, but by a considerable amount of rather obnoxious snickering.

Ladies who operated Type-Writers were quickly nicknamed "typewriters."

They didn't care much for the word.

They felt that it was a little flippant, as it was.

But the problem of finding a more suitable term was hard. "Secretary" didn't seem right because a secretary, if not a desk for writing, was a man. A secretary might employ a girl to type the correspondence, but a secretary could not wear a shirtwaist to work.

"Stenographer" was wrong, too, because a stenographer was an expert in taking dictation in Gregg or Pitman shorthand notes, not necessarily a typist at all.

No one had yet thought of "typist."

"Typewriter" was pretty good, and, for the next quarter century, "typewriter" was the word.

The double meaning was manna for all wits, cards and stage comedians, for it was almost impossible to mention the word in a leering tone of voice without getting a laugh. Magazines and joke books had a fine time with it. A fair sample was the story about the young businessman who had suffered a sudden reverse and wrote to his wife: "Dear Blanche: I have sold off all my office furniture, chairs, desks, etc., etc., and I am writing this letter under difficulties with my typewriter on my lap."

A cartoon of the period showed two men in an office looking thoughtfully at a Remington Model 4. The caption:

WALLER: Cracky! What a pretty typewriter you have!

HICKS: Pretty! She's angelic. Why, man, when that girl taps off an ordinary letter on that dusty old machine, you'd think you were listening to a symphony from Beethoven.

The typewriter gags were not entirely unfriendly, just slightly over on the contemptuous side. They did not discourage other young ladies from following in the footsteps of the pioneer eight—or, if they did, the results were statistically invisible. The YWCA continued to turn out typewriters (female) as fast as it could. Its classes grew in size and spread to other branches all over the country. Wyckoff, Seamans & Benedict instantly realized that they had seen the future and she worked. Remington schools were opened as fast as was feasible, and, although there

The Artist of 1875 Shows the Horrors That Would Follow if Women Were Permitted to Engage in Office Work

was no overt discrimination against males, the student bodies were overwhelmingly female. Private typing schools sprouted throughout the nation, and established shorthand and secretarial teachers rushed to add typing to their curricula.

There were tens of thousands of American women eager to have a job, and the Type-Writer had suddenly opened a new opportunity. Many women were working in factories, schools, stores, in domestic service and on farms. But, with only a few exceptions, there was nothing a young lady with some education, and some pretension towards white-collaredness, could do. She could teach school. She could be a nurse. It was practically impossible for her to invade man's world, the whole fascinating apparatus of business and commerce, which was where she especially wanted to be.

Typing was an invasion route into that world, and, from 1882 on, the traffic clogged the highway. It was Wyckoff, Seamans & Benedict's great good fortune, at the beginning of the stampede, to be selling the one and only typewriter on the market. They were caught in something bigger than the three of them, and they did all they could to increase its size. One thing they did was invent the public typist-stenographer. They stationed young ladies with Remingtons in the best hotels in the leading cities, suggesting that top-flight business executives were so sold on typewriting that they needed a typewriter's service when they were traveling. In a few cases, business executives actually did feel that way. Many more, seeing the Remington girl and her pretty work, realized for the first time how nice it would be, and how efficient, to have a combination of the same sort in their own outer offices. Numbers of the girls, realizing that they were taking in quite a lot of money, saw that they could go into business on their own. What had started as a promotional stunt quickly developed into a genuine, thriving business. Wyckoff, Seamans & Benedict were not unhappy, for whenever another typing service opened its doors it had to own at least one Type-Writer.

Public stenography attracted many of the first typewriters, but a majority headed straight for regular, salaried employment in business and professional offices in the downtown districts of the nearest, biggest cities. Sometimes the going was a little rough, as it is for all pioneers. It was difficult to be the first girl in an office where there had never been a girl before. The boss, as a rule, was not as sure as he had been about the wisdom of hiring a girl to work shoulder to shoulder with his male employees, and the whole office had its doubts about whether typewriting, in itself, was a valid technique. Male clerks, copyists, stenographers and office boys, in general, realized that the new typewriter represented some sort of threat to their own job security.

It could be embarrassing. In the opening chapters of a novel, *The Typewriter Girl*, by Olive Pratt Rayner, the heroine, Juliet Appleton, an American typewriter of twenty-two, down on her luck in London, but honest and the owner of a Barlock, is applying at the offices of Flor & Fingelman, on Southampton Row, in answer to a newspaper advertisement, "Shorthand and Typewriter (female) wanted."

It is a nerve-wracking scene:

> Three clerks (male), in seedy black coats, the eldest with hair the color of a fox's, went on chaffing one another for two minutes after I closed the door, with ostentatious unconsciousness of my insignificant presence. . . . The youngest, after a while, wheeled around on his high stool and broke out with the chivalry of his age and class, "Well, what's your business?"
>
> My voice trembled a little, but I mustered up courage and spoke. "I have called about your advertisement. . . ."
>
> He eyed me up and down. I am slender, and, I will venture to say, if not pretty, at least interesting looking.

"How many words a minute?" he asked after a long pause. I stretched the truth as far as its elasticity would permit. "Ninety-seven," I answered. . . .

The eldest clerk, with the foxy head, wheeled around, and took his turn to stare. He had hairy hands and large goggle-eyes. . . . I detected an undercurrent of double meaning. . . . I felt disagreeably like Esther in the presence of Ahasuerus—a fat and oily Ahasuerus of fifty. . . . He perused me up and down with his small pig's eyes, as if he were buying a horse, scrutinizing my face, my figure, my hands, my feet. I felt like a Circassian in an Arab slavemarket. . . .

Miss Rayner, needless to say, was writing fiction, and her main intent was to tickle the reader's emotions (in the next chapters, for sensationalism's own sake, she sent Juliet Appleton, riding a bicycle, wearing a weird pair of pedal-pushers, and believing fervently in Darwinism, to spend a hectic fortnight in an experimental community run by Anarchists of a Bakunin stripe all of whom try to make off with her two-wheeler), but there was a germ of truth in her imaginary account.

In fact, Miss Elise Diehl, whose place in typewriter history is secure because two decades later, in 1904, she organized the first union of its kind, the Stenographers' and Typewriters' Union No. 11655, AF of L, when she sent out the first call for the first meeting, announced that there was more on her agenda than hours, wages, working conditions, and fringe benefits: "Professional services, instead of 'Companionship,' in business offices, is one of the main matters that should receive our attention."

There is no doubt that Miss Diehl, despite her loose sentence structure, meant to say that stenographers and typewriters ought not to be asked to take more than dictation.

However rudely man may have behaved towards the early typewriters, he was not hostile. Offices that had been the type-

A Typist of the 1880's on Her Way to Work

writer salesman's despair began ordering writing machines by
the dozen as soon as tycoons understood that, like the well-
worn automobile selling joke of later years, the model actually
was to accompany the product. Men who had scoffed at $125 as
an outrageously large price seemed to revise their opinions when
they learned that, for another $600 or so a year, they could em-
ploy a girl to operate the machine. It was, in fact, an absurdly
low salary, as Miss Diehl, among others, pointed out. Ungallant
though it was, part of the girls' popularity was their willingness
to work for starvation wages. A top-flight, experienced girl
typist-secretary might earn $20 a week; a man with comparable
skill, doing exactly the same work, was paid at least $30. In
1888, at New Orleans, the members of the Women's Club listened to a talk by a guest speaker, Harry Hodgson, on the wonderful new opportunities the typewriter had created. He
described the average day of the average girl: she didn't have
to be at work until 8:30; she was allowed a full half-hour for
lunch; she was through by 5:30. And moreover, Hodgson said,
if she was reasonably proficient, she could expect to start at $6
a week. Instead of forming an emergency committee to aid girl
typists, the New Orleans ladies agreed that this was the best
break women had had for centuries.

They were not far wrong, if they were wrong at all. Shop
girls in 1888 were getting $6 a week as a top salary, and expert
saleswomen not more than $12. In time an expert typewriter
could work up to $20 a week and, for the most part, she was al-
lowed to sit down. Furthermore, by 1888, a handful of typewriters had gone from typing into private secretaryships, and
were acting, in effect, as their bosses' assistants. Perhaps they
were underpaid, but at least they were getting something like
man-sized salaries. Their success stories were widely publicized.
That hit-the-jackpot element, for girls with real career ambi-
tions, was most attractive. There were sixty thousand typewrit-

ers (female) in 1888, and, except for those who planned to marry the boss, most of them hoped to become his confidential, well-paid, business assistant.

The art of teaching typing boomed, not only in the United States but the world around, for Wyckoff, Seamans & Benedict were in earnest about worldwide distribution, and, as they established dealerships in one country after another (Germany, 1883; France, 1884; England, 1886; Belgium, 1886; Italy, 1889), they also started schools to train operators. At the same time, they urged the local sales agent to work the celebrity angle, hoping to catch another name as newsworthy as Mark Twain's. They caught quite a few. In England the best-known Remington user was Lloyd George, who had learned to type when he was a struggling Welsh attorney. But the Petrograd salesman came up with the most spectacular big name, Count Lyof Nikolayevitch Tolstoy, a man who loathed modern machinery in every form ("The most powerful weapon of ignorance—the diffusion of printed matter."—*War and Peace*, Epilogue, Part II, Chapter 8), and got a great photograph of the author, looking quite miserable, dictating to his daughter, Alexandra Lvovna, who sat poised over the Remington keyboard.

6 / Inventors are Never Satisfied

Foresight is a quality common to all inventors. Few, however, have as much of it as they can use, and since at the time none of the other writing-machine experimenters appreciated the historic significance of what Sholes, Glidden, Soule and the rest had done, invention continued at an accelerating clip, as if nothing had happened.

John Pratt, for instance, was as confident as ever that the printing-wheel principle was right. He continued to work along that line, ignoring the Kleinsteuber group's contributions and overlooking the insulting fact that his rivals had been inspired by what they considered Pratt's failures. Pratt patented an improved pterotype, still featuring a wheel with type arranged around its perimeter, in 1868, about a month after the Sholes-Glidden-Soule patent had been granted. Thomas A. Edison, inspired, in turn, by what he considered the inadequacies of the Kleinsteuber group's efforts, agreed with Pratt. He liked the printing-wheel theory. He added the idea of operating it electrically, and got a patent on such a device in 1872. Others favored the cylinder or sleeve principle, a modification of the wheel idea. Lucien S. Crandall, of Groton, New York, was among them. His 1881 machine had no type bars, and it didn't have a wheel, either, but the type was fixed in half a dozen bands or rings around a cylinder. When the operator pressed down one of the keys, the cylinder shifted laterally and rotated, selecting the proper band and the desired letter, bringing it to the printing point, and then pressing it against the paper. The cylinder amounted to six small type wheels, in short, and it was

Pratt's "Pterotype," 1868

much more compact than one big wheel. Cylinders could be changed, furthermore, without too much trouble, which meant that one could switch from one type face to another; if the operator grew tired of pica, he could change cylinders and try writing élite.

Even after the Remington appeared on the market, the other inventors showed no signs of slowing down. They seemed stimulated, rather than downcast, by the news that a writing machine was actually being manufactured. Jenne and Clough, none the less, had set a high standard for them to meet or try to beat. The Sholes-Glidden-Soule model had given them excellent raw material and, although the two Remington technicians considered themselves mere mechanics rather than inventors, their work showed uncanny discretion. Somehow they managed to keep all that was best about the Sholes-Glidden-Soule, adding other inventors' notions besides several of their own, and still turn out a composite that was simple and practical. It could be manufactured to sell for $125. Most of the bugs that had haunted the Kleinsteuber group were gone. The Type-Writer worked well and, with reasonable care on the operator's part, it was reasonably reliable.

Model 1, with its charming flowers and sewing-machine pedestal, had gone into production in a big hurry. Jenne and Clough had not had time, during the rush, to do much experimenting. It was the Remington Model 4, which went on sale in 1878, that represented the full Jenne-Clough treatment. The machine had a key shift and, for the first time, wrote lower-case as well as capital letters. It was crude by today's standards, needless to say, but it was a typewriter, and no doubt about it. Although other inventors continued to fool around with hopelessly impractical typewriter theories for years to come, the Model 4 incorporated only one really wrong idea. That was the under-strike principle. The printing point was still out of sight,

Lucien Crandall's Printing Cylinder Machine, 1881

directly beneath the main roller. The operator couldn't see the line he was working on. Yet when one considers that typewriter manufacture was only five years old, and when one thinks how absurd the first commercial radios, automobiles, or airplanes now appear, the one big Jenne-Clough error seems less remarkable than the number of times they were right.

Rival inventors were not that charitable. A cylinder-theory fancier, James B. Hammond, who had studied to be a minister but had actually worked as a court reporter and as a *New York Tribune* Civil War correspondent, took a long, critical look at the Model 4 Remington and, although he wasn't particularly upset about its lack of visibility, concluded that it wouldn't do.

He thought its press work was sloppy, with some letters darker than others because the operator couldn't help hitting the keys with finger blows of unequal strength. He thought its keyboard was poorly arranged. He believed that a typewriter should have several interchangeable type faces. Hammond figured that a cylinder-type machine would answer all three of the criticisms he raised.

He was not entirely wrong, for he parlayed an initial investment of $5,000 into something more than $1,000,000. The Hammond typewriter was good. It won devoted friends the world around. It included several ingenious notions. The first model, starting in 1881, had a hammer which hit the reverse side of the paper from behind, pressing it against the type cylinder; and, since the velocity of the hammer's blow did not depend upon the operator's finger strength, and each strike was delivered with exactly the force of all others, a complete novice could turn out beautifully even typing. The Hammond's keyboard was gracefully curved. The arrangement of the keys was more rational than the Remington's. The type cylinder could be changed, a feature that was popular with typists who wrote lots of letters in foreign languages.

At the same time it would be inaccurate to say that Hammond was entirely correct. The Remington also did well, and ultimately the entire industry agreed, at the public's insistence, that type bars and not type cylinders are best; and that keyboards should be rectangular, not curved; and that keys should be arranged in the way that Sholes, Glidden, Soule, Jenne and Clough had arranged them.

In 1883, E. E. Horton's patent proposed a partial solution to the visibility problem. His model brought the printing point out from directly under the roller, but only about half the distance to where it is now. It was an improvement, and with it Horton became Canada's first typewriter manufacturer, with a plant

The 1884 Hammond

---

at Toronto. The trouble was that the operator still couldn't see what he was writing. In 1889, Charles Spiro tried for visibility another way. In his Barlock, the type bars stuck almost straight up in the air in their position of rest, and hit down on the top surface of the roller. Unfortunately, the type bars were just long enough to block the operator's view. In order to see what he had written, he had to lean forward and peer over the small type-bar fence. In 1890, John N. Williams came very close with a variation on the top-strike. Instead of merely swinging to the printing point, the Williams type bars jumped at it like so many grasshoppers, traveling low and fast. The operator, for the first time, could see the word he was writing and the line he was working on without performing any gymnastics. The trouble was that as soon as he had turned up the paper to start a new line, the old line disappeared behind the roller. He knew what he was saying, all right, but he had to rely on his memory to tell him what he had said.

A front-strike action was the solution. Two different versions of it were patented in 1887. Neither was manufactured, but they were the first in a series of visible machines that included, by 1896, the Underwood. Remington was not particularly concerned about visibility. The Remington was the leader by a wide margin, and typists didn't seem to be as much interested in visibility as inventors were.

Remington didn't appear particularly worried, either, by the activities of W. P. Kidder, of Jamaica Plain, Massachusetts. Kidder thought that the noisiness of the Remington and the several Remington-type machines on the market was a great weakness, and he set out, starting in 1896, to manufacture a machine called the Noiseless. The idea was to keep the type bar from slapping hard against the roller. Kidder believed that by using a toggle-cam, a gadget to limit the type bar's action, he could change the hard slap into a firm, quiet push. It sounded easier, to hear Kidder tell it, than it really was. There were twenty long years, and hard ones, before Kidder's Noiseless reached the market.

It was safe enough for Remington to ignore Kidder. But the Underwood, designed by H. L. and F. X. Wagner, was another story. In an odd, indirect way, Densmore and Yost were responsible for Underwood. After Densmore and Yost had sold Philo Remington the Sholes-Glidden-Soule and had served briefly as the Remington's sales agents, it occurred to their highly creative minds that the world really needed more than just one typewriter. Densmore went back to Sholes and persuaded him to start working on a design for a portable writing machine. Yost went to Franz Wagner, whom he considered the most brilliant of typewriter inventors after Sholes, and talked him into working on an office-size machine, the Caligraph. It was to be a good deal like the Remington, but with several original features all its own, including a double-size keyboard so that it could write upper- and lower-case characters without using a shift.

The Remington Typewriter Company took a poor view of Yost's and Densmore's energetic activities. The Sholes portable, in particular, distressed Remington, because it bore such a strong family resemblance to the Remington itself. Since the promoters were drawing royalties on the Sholes-Glidden-Soule patents they didn't want to make Remington too angry, so they stopped working on it. In 1893 there was a big combination. Remington, Densmore, Yost and the four Smith brothers, Wilbert, Lyman C., Monroe C. and Hurlbut, joined hands, rather uneasily, to create the Union Typewriter Company of America. It was like a whale joining forces with a school of minnows, and Caligraph was soon lost in the jostling that ensued.

The Yost Typewriter of 1885

That left Franz Wagner an inventor without a company. He looked around for a good new idea, something quite unlike a Remington, and he and his brother, H. L., came up with a visible front-strike design. John T. Underwood, whose father, John Underwood, had been a pioneer in the ribbons and carbons business, bought the Wagners' machine. Production began in 1895 in a tiny shop, with a floor space twenty feet wide and one hundred feet long, on Hudson Street, New York City. Underwood got off to a fast start. Within a year the factory filled a whole four-story building in Bayonne, New Jersey. Three years later, in 1899, when Underwood moved to Hartford, Connecticut, it needed a plant three times as big as the Bayonne place—all before Underwood introduced its sensationally popular Model 5.

To make life all the more difficult for Remington, the four talented Smith brothers pulled out of the combine in 1903. They thought that Union Typewriter should be manufacturing a visible and, having lost the argument, they decided to go out as independents and make it by themselves. The Smiths began by turning out a Model 2, which was pretty confusing, especially when they followed it, after about a year, with a Model 1. Carl Gabrielson designed them both and they bore the rather cumbersome name, L. C. Smith & Bros. Typewriter. (L. C. got the top billing because he was the eldest.) When the Smith brothers hopped aboard the front-strike bandwagon, they wanted the world to know about it. Their plant in Syracuse adjoined the New York Central tracks, and they put up eighteen big billboards along their property to catch the train passengers' attention. The signs carried slogans like, "Writing in Sight Is in Line with Progress," and "When Precedent and Progress Clash, We Forsake Precedent," and, "You Are Right Side Up; Why Write Upside Down?". To train passengers who had been paying close attention to the technological shop talk of the typewriter industry, these pithy remarks were easily understandable. But they must have puzzled those who had never heard of the visibility controversy, especially passengers who thought that L. C. Smith & Bros. were cough-drop manufacturers.

A timid inventor might have said to himself, at this point, that the writing machine had been developed about as far as it could go. Timidity, however, was one of the last words that could be used to describe Edward B. Hess, of New York, a former silk salesman and a brilliant tinkerer with mechanical gadgets. Hess was the president of a firm called Precision Mechanical Laboratories with offices at 125 White Street in lower Manhattan. The laboratories, upon examination, did not entirely live up to their grandiose name. There was only one, to begin with, and it was an ordinary machine shop on the top floor of a small loft building. The quality of the work done there, while good, had set no records for precision.

On the other hand, Hess was the sort of man who could turn a plain machine shop into what seemed like a precision laboratory simply by walking through the door and waving the magic wand of his personality. He was tall and built along the lines of a fifty-gallon oil drum. He had a total-recall memory, and a preference for recalling Shakespeare, among authors, and grand opera, among musical forms. Hess boasted that if anyone started a Shakespeare quotation or an operatic aria, he could finish it. There is no evidence that he was ever stumped. As one who had earned a living selling fabrics, he appreciated silk shirting and fine suiting, especially when the colors were loud. Hess's idea of a good combination, for general laboratory work, was a bold hound's-tooth checked suit with a peppermint-stick striped shirt.

Hess was not an engineer, and some of his favorite ideas were enough to drive engineers mad, but he was fortunate in having, as a colleague, a small, quiet, disciplined, conservative technician, Lewis C. Meyers, who had had considerable experience with typewriters. Meyers had worked for the Brady Manufacturing Company in Brooklyn. He'd been associated with other inventors. He had built experimental models for the Williams Typewriter Company. It was Meyers who actually ran the Precision Mechanical Laboratories and its small staff, and it was Meyers who listened while the ebullient Hess sparked off ideas at a furious rate. Whereupon, as far as possible, Meyers translated the inspired dreams into mechanical reality.

Hess looked over the typewriter field and concluded that, while Underwood and L. C. Smith were right in their emphasis on visibility, and despite Remington's powerful hold on typewriter selling, there was still room for a writing machine that matched his own ideas about what a writing machine should be. He agreed with Kidder that typewriter press work was less than perfect. He was very strong for visibility and for the front-strike, but he didn't like the clutter of the existing visibles—knobs, bars, ribbon mechanism and other projections—that spoiled the operator's clear view without actually blocking it. He thought that typewriter repair costs were altogether too high, and that, by improved design, they could be cut. Above all else, he thought that a typewriter could work a lot more easily from the operator's point of view. With all this in mind, Hess put aside the work he was doing on an automatic envelope-sealer, and concentrated on a new, improved typewriter.

The first of the 140 typewriter patents Hess was granted during his lifetime was, in his own words, a "freak" form of visible, and nothing came of it. Immediately thereafter, however, he invented a score of improvements, and, with Meyers' help, incorporated them into four demonstration models.

The most obvious difference between the Hess typewriter and the machines on the market was its light, fast touch. Several ideas had gone into the improvement. Hess had invented a type-bar action that began by moving slowly when the operator started to press the key and accelerated rapidly as the key continued down. He had turned the linkage around, so that the action was a pull rather than push, which was an energy-saving innovation. And he'd taken much of the friction out of the escapement, the toothed wheel that links the keys with the carriage and moves it along one space, no more or less, every time a letter is struck.

The typists who tried out the experimental models didn't understand what Hess and Meyers had done. They only knew that the new machine had a marvelously light action. And that the press work was excellent. The accelerated type bars really flew to the printing point, and the impressions they made were sharp and clear.

Hess and Meyers had worked out a total of twenty new ideas, including a friction-free, ball-bearing, one-track rail to support the weight of the carriage as it moved back and forth, a new paper feed, a shield to keep erasure crumbs from falling down into the nest of type bars, and total, uncompromised visibility.

It was a great performance, all in all, and Hess and Meyers felt confident—as had all the typewriter inventors since Burt— that their Royal typewriter would instantly find someone with money to start production. A more accurate view of the situation was expressed by Hess's pet dogs. Hess had a passion for black-and-tans, the miniature lap dogs then at their peak of popularity. He owned as many as eight at one time, and he kept most of them in a tower room in his house at Bensonhurst, Long Island, which had a flight of tiny steps built to fit the dogs' tiny legs. Every day, when he came into the Precision Mechanical Laboratories, he brought at least one, and often two, of his pets with him. He worked with dogs on top of his desk, or in his large arms, and although they were a great nuisance to everyone else, no one dared complain for fear that, without a dog or two at hand, Hess might stop inventing. The black-and-tans showed not the slightest interest in Hess's typewriter. Neither, for a time, did anyone else. With a lawsuit threatening, plagued by lack of capital, and disheartened by the world's initial disinterest in the best typewriter yet devised, the Precision Mechanical Laboratories folded up. The Royal came within a hair's breadth of dying at birth.

The man who rescued the infant was Thomas Fortune Ryan, a specialist in picking winners at times when the odds against them were fantastically long, and a multimillionaire with an unparalleled record for not making public statements. According to an associate, William C. Whitney, Ryan was "the most adroit, suave and noiseless man" he had ever known. In 1874, when he was all of twenty-three years old, Ryan had bought a seat on the New York Stock Exchange. He had risen to a position of great power in Wall Street during the ensuing thirty years. His name had appeared in the newspapers time and time again as a participant in one huge deal after another. Yet in his entire career he had talked to reporters only twice, giving them formal statements that averaged ten lines of news-column space apiece. He had put the Southern Railway together out of a mélange of smaller railroad lines, and he had made an announcement about that. He had bought control of the Equitable Life Insurance Company for $2,500,000, and had allowed himself a few words on that occasion. But he hadn't said anything, for instance, when he gathered together several floundering tobacco companies, reorganized them, and joined them into one new outfit which he called, without much originality, American Tobacco. And he didn't say a word to the press when he handed Hess and Meyers $220,000 and told them to go ahead with the Royal typewriter.

Hess and Meyers went right to work. Their new shop was at Liberty Street, Brooklyn, and they were soon turning out machines, beginning with a model called the Royal Grand.

The Royal Typewriter, 1906

Ryan's backing was a great asset, especially when it came to building up the new company's staff. As one old typewriter hand has phrased it, Hess and Meyers had twenty-one arguments to use in behalf of Royal: twenty exclusive features and T. F. Ryan. The combination was enormously attractive to a lot of good, experienced typewriter men, who left established firms to join the new company. And, usually, when Royal captured a typewriter celebrity, the celebrity brought talent with him. E. J. Manning, for example, left Underwood in 1907 to become Royal's general manager. Royal got Charles C. Cook, Manning's assistant at Underwood, as a dividend. And Cook, who ran the Royal factory at Hartford from 1911, and is still an active director, was a key figure in the firm's ultimate success.

7 / Salesmen and Thieves

Typewriters were actually sold by typewriter salesmen. It was door-to-door work, except that the doors, for the most part, belonged to business offices rather than private homes. The going was rough. Remington's monopolistic position had been challenged as soon as it appeared that numbers of businesses were likely to adopt typewriting; the ten years during which "Remington Type-Writer" and "typewriter" were synonyms ended in 1883 when the Caligraph, a product of Yost's American Writing Machine Company, appeared. From the moment that there were two typewriters instead of only one, the salesmen who worked for Wyckoff, Seamans & Benedict were on their mettle, fighting to stave off the inroads of the eager beavers selling Caligraphs. In 1890, the Smith Brothers got into the act with their Smith Premier. Densmore, with the Densmore, was right on their heels. And from there on, despite the combination in 1893 into the alliance known as the Union Typewriter Company, a typewriter salesman's life was never placid. Or, at least, placid typewriter salesmen were soon looking around for some other line of work. As soon as Union failed in its effort to control the competition, new typewriters began breaking out all over. By 1909 there were a total of eighty-nine separate typewriter companies in the United States alone. Royal, which was designed in 1904, is the youngest typewriter that still survives, but well over a hundred post-Royal firms were started, nearly all of them in the decade 1905–1915. A Blickensderfer salesman who preferred long stops for coffee to pounding his route had to face the fact that, during his second cup, the race might be won by a rival representing Acme, Alexander, Allen, American, Atlas, Barlock, Bennett, Bennington, Blake, Brooks, Century, Chicago, Commercial Visible, Corona, Cram, Crandall, Crown, Darling, Daugherty, Demountable, Densmore, Dollar, Duplex, Edland, Elliott-Fisher, Ellis, Emerson, Essex, Fay-Sholes, Federal, Ford, Fountain, Fox, Franklin, Garbell, Hammond, Harris, Hartford, Hooven, International, Jackson, Jewett, Junior, Keystone, McCall, Manograph, Merritt, Molle, Monarch, Moon-Hopkins, Morris, Munson, National, Nickerson, Noiseless, Odell, Official, Oliver, People's, Pittsburgh, Postal, Rapid, Reliance, Remington, Rex, Royal, Schiesari, Secor, Sholes Visible, L. C. Smith, Smith Premier, Stearns, Sterling, Sun, Taylor, Triumph, Type-Adder, Underwood, Victor, Visigraph, Walker, Williams, Woodstock, World, Yost, or Yu Ess, among others. Not to mention the danger of losing a sale to one of the leading imported machines like Adler, A.E.G., Ideal, Kappel, Mercedes, Mignon, Regina, Saxonia, Titania, Torpedo and Urania from Germany, Empire from Canada, Hermes from Switzerland, Hesperia, Olivetti and Vittoria from Italy, Imperial, Salter and Wellington from England, Contin and M.A.P. from France, or Japy from Japan.

It was surely enough to make a man nervous, but if 1910's typewriter salesman was distressed about the extent of the competition he hid his anxiety from the world. On the surface he appeared to be immoderately self-confident, a confirmed optimist certain that he lived in the best of all possible worlds and that, paradoxically, things were getting better, in every way, day by day. He would work like a maniac to close a single sale. One typewriter salesman, for example, called on a small neighborhood jewelry store in New York City, and found that the jeweler was not in the least hospitable, because two other representatives of two other firms had already been in and both had insisted on leaving typewriters on approval. The jeweler was fed up. As he had pointed out to salesman number one, he had practically no correspondence, and the little he had could be handled perfectly well with pen and ink. In the second place, he didn't know how to operate a typewriter and had no intention of learning. There just wasn't room in the shop for a third demonstration typewriter, especially since he wasn't planning to test even brands one and two.

Salesman number three agreed not to leave his sample. In the face of this formidable set of resistances he might well have decided to cross the jewelry store off his list of prospects. On the contrary, he made some notes, went home, and, according to his own account, stayed up half the night working on an angle.

He was back on the jeweler's doorstep the next morning. He had with him the product of his nocturnal labors: a complete set of showcase price-and-description cards, neatly typed in solid caps, for the major items in the jeweler's stock. "You see, sir," the salesman said, "this machine can do a lot for you besides helping with your correspondence . . . ."

The jeweler was licked, of course. The sale was concluded in a few minutes. It is small wonder, with nearly a hundred typewriter companies employing thousands of travelers, many imbued with spirit of that sort, that the total typewriter sales record was broken year after year with monotonous regularity; the

A Salesman Can't Ignore the Typist

TYPEWRITER AND SECRETARY

mystery is how American businessmen held back enough money to purchase anything except typewriters. Leaving a writing machine on trial was the standard procedure. Wyckoff, Seamans & Benedict had started the fashion, a natural companion to the scheme of delivering complimentary typewriters to big shots in the hope of nabbing a free testimonial. In the 'seventies, 'eighties and even the 'nineties, the free-trial offer had been most appropriate; potential buyers needed time to assure themselves that the machine would really and truly work. They wanted to be left alone with it so that they could consider it from all sides, poke at it, and try writing on it in complete privacy. Wyckoff, Seamans & Benedict had therefore instructed their salesmen not to try for anything, on a first call, except permission to leave one of the curiosity-breeding gadgets behind. By 1910, on the other hand, the typewriter had pretty well proved itself, and yet the free-trial offer remained the prevailing selling method. No firm dared abandon it for fear that if its salesmen didn't leave a demonstration machine, another's would. Typewriter men have cursed the method for half a century, for it is clumsy and expensive, yet it remains the dominant mode, at least as far as selling office standards and electrics is concerned. (Portables, which are a category unto themselves, are now considered home appliances and are handled, like pop-up toasters or rotisserie-broilers, through retail home-appliance stores.) The drawbacks of the free-trial-offer system are many. A certain percentage of mankind will gladly agree to try out anybody's typewriter without any intention of buying, fiddle around with it just enough to scratch the finish or mar the roller, and then report—as is their perfect legal right—that it won't do. Great chefs, according to rumor, think highly of restaurant patrons who inspect the planked steak for four, sniff, and then send it back to the kitchen to be done over. Typewriter men share none of that point of view. Yet there is not much that they can do about the system except in times of severe typewriter shortage, like the years immediately after World War II, when typewriters didn't have to be sold at all and the problem was trying to catch up with back orders. Typewriter trade journals and office-appliance reviews, during the 1905–1915 period, commented bitterly on the abuses of the free-trial offer. The "magazine of office equipment," *Office Appliances,* was particularly exercised about businessmen who would accept a typewriter on trial and then stall around endlessly before deciding whether to return it or come across with the cash. An editorial captioned, "Don't Deny The Traveling Man," said:

> Members of the traveling fraternity frequently complain about the scant courtesy they receive from buyers, who by constant procrastination keep them on expense for days at a time before they are ready to see the salesman and talk business. . . . There should be some way of impressing the fact upon buyers that the traveling men come a long way to see them; that their time belongs to their employers; and that the hotel bills and incidental expenses amount to a considerable figure.

By accepting one free trial after another, as was pointed out, an unscrupulous scoundrel could operate a small business for a long time before exhausting the patience of all the firms on the scene and, during the period, enjoy one handsome new typewriter after another without ever paying a cent for the privilege. And, as if bad-mannered buyers were not bad enough, the generosity of the system and the zeal of competing salesmen provided a field day for outright crooks. A scoundrel with almost any sort of address could order two or three typewriters on approval, knowing that his credit and reputation would not be checked carefully, if at all. In most cities he could expect delivery by the following morning. He then had at least a week in which he could dispose of the property and make his getaway. One confirmed typewriter stealer, for instance, was Charles W.

Willersdorf, who operated in New Hampshire, Massachusetts and Connecticut, according to *Typewriter Topics,* which began publication in September, 1905, the first trade paper devoted exclusively to typewriter affairs which was not a house organ. *Typewriter Topics* featured a regular column of intelligence about typewriter thieves and their methods. Willersdorf, it reported, was ostensibly a magazine-subscription salesman and a book agent, a "small, spare fellow weighing about 125 pounds" and "a smooth talker," who had a knack for making friends quickly and easily and a lamentable tendency to forget to turn in the money from subscriptions and book sales to the publishers he represented. One of Willersdorf's mistakes led to another. The publishers, in time, would find out about his forgetfulness and drive Willersdorf into his second bad habit, which was ordering a typewriter on approval intending all the time to pawn or sell it. A warrant was out for his arrest.

Typewriter stealing was common enough so that Philip K. Sweet, a private detective with offices at 1133 Broadway, New York, made a specialty of tracking down writing-machine thieves. Sweet had previously been a member of the United States Secret Service. In addition to his job of catching typewriter crooks, he edited "The Detective's Department" in *Typewriter Topics* and was a regular advertiser. He found himself in a curious dilemma, for on one hand he wanted all typewriter men to realize the situation's seriousness and to take note of the alarming growth of typewriter thefts, and on the other hand he hoped to explain that, with Philip K. Sweet on the job, there was nothing to worry about. In a single issue he'd describe the cunning of some new larcenist in his column and then, a few pages farther along, his advertisement would assure the world that the country's leading typewriter detective had the criminals hog-tied. Sweet was proud of his methods, such as the identification of a machine by close examination of a sample of its printing. He praised the new system of engraving serial numbers on all typewriters, making the eradication of their identifying marks quite difficult. Scientific detective work, he felt sure, was about to bring the era of the typewriter thief to an end. Meanwhile, with something approaching masochistic pleasure, he called his readers' attention to the fact that the crime wave had taken another alarming upturn.

Unhappily for Sweet's optimistic prediction, typewriters remain a favorite thieves' target. A talented young artist with a studio in mid-Manhattan was robbed in November, 1953. A sneak thief broke into her place, filled with paintings she was getting ready for a show, and made off with only one object: her well-worn portable typewriter. In 1951, also in New York City, thieves stole several hundred dollars' worth of machines using the Willersdorf gambit exactly, with a few up-to-date touches. Two men who said they were television producers and script writers, and had an impressive embossed business card to prove it, rented a small office on West Fourteenth Street. The center of television activity is a good thirty-five blocks distant, and yet it was not completely impossible that they wanted to work at a little remove from the maelstrom. In every respect except location, the men seemed right for their self-announced roles. They were nervous. They paced back and forth like incipient ulcer cases in the empty three-room suite, waiting, they said, for the office furniture to be delivered. They were sharply critical of the paint, and they made the landlord change it from one bilious shade of green to another. They ordered four telephones and six typewriters. They did not actually give anyone any cash, but they paid three months' rent in advance, by check, and a deposit on the phones, by check, and they added one touch that seemed to prove they really were in show business: they hired a cleaning man to straighten up the place after hours, and agreed, casually, to pay him $35 a week for a total of about five hour's work. By the end of the second day, all Fourteenth Street between Seventh and Eighth Avenues had heard about the high-powered tenants and was duly impressed. The typewriters arrived on the third day, shortly before noon. By five o'clock the police were on the scene, summoned by the landlord who had heard from his bank that the check was no good and had discovered that his tenants and the typewriters had disappeared.

The traffic in stolen typewriters was a form of compliment, however loathsome, and the free-trial offer, even if it did encourage larceny, worked far more often than it failed. By 1910, according to a most conservative estimate by a typewriter historian, George Carl Mares, there were two million typewriters in use in the United States and about one-third of them were operated by young ladies gainfully employed for the purpose. The number of patents issued in class 197, typewriting machines, was well past the 2,600 mark (proving again that inventors are indefatigable), and most of the large-circulation magazines would no longer read unsolicited manuscripts in pen and ink. The typewriter had become a great favorite among newspapermen, most of whom not only typed badly but regarded their lack of skill as preferable to knowing something about the new tool of their trade. (Years later, in a similar mood of perversity, there were newspapermen ready to argue, in all seriousness, that a graduate degree in journalism was a handicap to a newspaper career.) Arthur Brisbane, editor-in-chief of the *New York Evening Journal*, Hart Lyman, editor-in-chief of the *New York Morning Tribune*, and William McCloy, managing editor of the *New York Evening Sun*, had been among the typewriting style leaders. McCloy was a conspicuous exception to the bad-typing rule. He had started on the *Sun* as a professional typewriter (male) and had worked up from taking dictation to ordering everybody around the city room. Edward W. Bok, the famous editor of the *Ladies' Home Journal,* was also a typing fan and an ex-stenographer who had made good, but most of his stenography, for Western Union, Henry Holt, and Charles Scribner's, had been shorthand rather than typing.

Most newspaper offices had no hard and fast rule about typewritten copy; reporters and rewrite men who liked the typewriter were encouraged to use it, but they were not compelled to do so. (On the distinguished English newspaper, the *Manchester Guardian,* that is the prevailing attitude today, except that the weight is slightly on the side of pen and ink. Reporters and leader writers who insist on typing are allowed to do so, but in a separate enclosure, apart from the main news room, so that they won't disturb the office.) It is interesting that the typewriter pioneers didn't think of journalists when they speculated about what professional classes would embrace the writing machine. They thought of authors, clergymen and telegraph

Early Sob Sisters at Work in a Newspaper Office

operators, but, as things turned out, no group, except professional typists, outranked newspapermen in its devotion to the typewriter. They became typewriter buffs, in the Mark Twain sense, almost as a matter of course. (The *Manchester Guardian* staff is a very special case; they are not so much anti-typewriter as pro the memory of the late C. P. Scott, the editor who won the provincial paper worldwide fame, and always wrote in longhand.)

Typewriter manufacturers and typewriter salesmen were pleased to have newspapermen enthusiastic about the product. Along with the idea that good reporters didn't type skillfully, however, went the theory that within the city room a battered machine was a sign of status, a form of reverse-English snobbism like dirty white shoes for winter wear at men's colleges in the Northeast. Typewriter salesmen soon realized that there was no sense in trying to sell new machines to a paper's editorial staff. The profitable attack was to focus on the business and advertising departments where there were secretaries who admired delicacy of touch, clarity of printing, and all the other niceties. After a machine had been used hard for five or six years, and had been beaten to such a frazzle that the girls in the classified billing department would no longer have anything to do with it, it was just about ripe for turning over to the paper's star reporter.

At salesmen's get-togethers, where the techniques of the business were argued and compared, a debate raged over whether it was better to carry a sample on initial calls or to travel empty-handed.

There was a lot to say on both sides.

The big argument against carrying a sample was the typewriter's weight, about twenty-five pounds. A salesman could knock himself out carrying the machine from one door to the next without ever getting to see a prospect. But there was some danger, if you won permission to leave a typewriter on trial and then had to go and get it, that the customer might lose interest in the interim and harden his heart against the whole enterprise before you got back.

Leaving aside the question of portage, many salesmen agreed that the best way to get permission to leave a machine was to walk in briskly with the baby in your arms, uncover it, and just let it sit there gleaming darkly. In case the prospect had never heard of a typewriter, you didn't have to attempt to describe what a typewriter was. In offices where typewriters were a novelty, the mere presence of the machine created an interested stir. In offices already equipped with typewriters, the girls would gather to coo over it because it was newer than the machines they were using. The boss would have to be a real ogre to make you pack it up and take it away when everyone was having so much fun with it and you were proposing to leave it, absolutely without obligation, and all for free. If your typewriter really was good, it of course sold itself within the course of the next few days. So that you might, using the storm-in-and-put-it-down technique, actually conclude a sale without making any pitch at all. And, if you lugged the big monsters around all day, every day, you might not have enough breath left to do otherwise.

The empty-handed school of thought reported that there was nothing better than leaving your typewriters checked at your hotel and going back to get one after you had permission to park it. The method was not only easier on the muscles of the arms and back, but it enabled you to walk right in through any firm's front door, in your Chesterfield and bowler hat, looking for all the world like a customer. "There's no danger that you'll be taken for a peddler," one expert salesman wrote in the correspondence columns of one of the trade papers, "and, by making your first contact empty-handed you avoid raising hostilities before you've even had a chance to open your mouth."

The following issue of the same journal contained a reply from a sample-carrying enthusiast. The empty-handed theories were all well and good, the second salesman wrote, for the weak and the lazy. He believed that a typewriter man should have a typewriter with him at all times. Why? Because during that very week he had sold two machines to pedestrians who had stopped him, on his way to make a call, and had asked him, unsuspectingly, what in the world he was carrying in the funny big black box.

All salesmen were agreed, early in the game, that the way to convince the boss was to convince the typist. "The girl is the buyer nine times out of ten," said the *Royal Standard* in its December, 1910, issue. "Get the good graces of the girls; it costs nothing and it pays well in the end." The advice was impeccable, as many men, including typewriter salesmen, had known for a long time.

It was true, and it is still generally true, that most of the time a typist who wanted one particular brand of typewriter very badly could get it. If she couldn't get it right away, she could get it when it was time to replace her worn-out machine. Typewriter salesmen, realizing that the girls cared more deeply than anyone else about which typewriters they used, tried not to underestimate their power. Manufacturers did the same—not only writing-machine manufacturers but companies making and selling all the accouterments of the stenographer's trade. For a time, Oliver gave away a handsome beveled-edge hand mirror to all lady operators whose bosses had bought them Olivers. Typewriter-ribbon manufacturers began packing their product in little round metal boxes, not that there was a whole lot to say for little round metal boxes (square boxes were easier to pack, stack and stamp, and cardboard was lighter and cheaper than metal), but because typists found little round metal boxes, after the ribbon had been removed, useful for holding paper clips, stamps or hairpins. To date, with only a few exceptions, ribbon manufacturers haven't dared change the package for fear of stirring up the dominant female's wrath. Royal, while it gave away no premiums, made the strongest of all bids for the secretary's favor; the fundamental inspiration behind Hess's design was operator comfort, and Royal was not at all shy about advertising its machines as the typewriter's typewriter.

A Happy Oliver Operator of 1907

From time to time, subsequently, various models of various makes have been popular with typists just because they were expensive. A de luxe machine might have extra features worth more than the difference in price, but whether it did or not, it served as tangible proof, sitting on a girl's desk, that the management liked her well enough to spend an extra $50 or so on her behalf. Girls who really didn't have any strong feelings about the technical features of the premium-priced model nevertheless demanded it as a token of personal status.

Salesmanship was directed from lower Manhattan. Most of the important companies did not manufacture in New York City, but if, in 1910, you had wanted to catch the up-to-date typewriter business shop talk you would not have gone to Hartford, Connecticut, or Ilion, New York, but to Typewriter Row, the stretch of Broadway from Park Place north past City Hall to Leonard Street, a distant of eight blocks. Many of the buildings were right on Broadway, but those that were not stood within half a block to the east or west. Among the firms that had huddled together in unprecedented concentration, in approximate order as you might stroll uptown, were Hammond, Blickensderfer, Underwood, Yost, Royal, Union, Fay-Sholes, Columbia-Barlock, Oliver, L. C. Smith, Stearns, Sun, Monarch, Remington, Fisher, Densmore, Wellington, Smith Premier and New Century. At lunch time on a sunny day the sidewalks were crowded with men and women talking about the latest sensation in the typewriter business, like the exploits of Mr. Charles Righter of Philadelphia, a typewriter salesman who developed fire-engine chasing to a specialty because, more often than not, clouds of smoke in the business district meant orders for replacements for the charred, twisted, typewriter victims, or the feats performed by Kittie Smith, who had learned to type better with her toes than many persons could with their fingers, and

Typist at Work with a Dictating Machine in 1890 (Storage Batteries under the Table)

was getting a big publicity play in the newspapers and magazines.

Typewriter Row establishments were, in most instances, both showrooms and business-office headquarters. Sales strategies and manufacturing policies were decided in the offices upstairs. On the street level were public showrooms, and the various companies struggled, in a dignified way, to look more impressive than their neighbors. The prevailing style of décor was expensive-solemn. The L. C. Smith office-showroom at 311 Broadway, for instance, was largely oak. The walls were paneled with oak from the floor up to about waist height, and covered with green burlap from there to the ceiling. The cabinets, desks and chairs were all oak. There were potted palms galore, and green velours curtains at the windows. There were only a couple of L. C. Smiths in sight, on the theory that it was psychologically more sound to display two than two hundred, as if the product were a rare jewel. If a customer brave enough to ask any questions showed up, he was led to the "demonstration area," a space separated from the rest of the establishment by hip-high, golden oak partitions with shiny brass railings and short green curtains running along their tops. Inside the secret enclosure was a semi-circular oak bench, where the customer sat. Inside the semi-circle stood a golden oak pedestal, and on the pedestal stood an L. C. Smith. Well-behaved customers were allowed to touch it, if they insisted, but the main idea was to have a professional demonstrator run the machine. For most visitors were not business executives at all, but merely tourists who had seen Wall Street and Trinity Church, had taken a quick look at City Hall, and merely wanted to see if the newfangled writing machines were as slick as the advertisements said.

8 / Race Against Time

The phrase "learning to type," as it is now used, means learning to type by touch using all eight fingers and both thumbs, although many non-professionals manage to operate the machine successfully with inferior techniques. The prolific writer Irwin Ross, for instance, goes like a bat out of a cave using only one finger *of one hand,* as if testing to see whether the keys are red hot. His is a most unusual method, for the average hunt-and-peck operator employs at least two fingers, or four, and may, from time to time, sneak in a fifth. Modern non-touch typists are modest about their abilities, however, and say, when questioned, "I don't *really* know how to type; I just use my own system."

By today's standards, no one knew how to type for fifteen years after the typewriter came onto the market. Ten-finger touch technique was not thought of until 1882, and it didn't catch on until 1888. An "expert" or "trained" operator, during all that time, was simply one familiar enough with the arrangement of the keys to go fairly fast, who understood what the various buttons, levers and keys were for, and who could change a ribbon or disengage a jammed type bar. Sholes himself belonged to this category and so did the various shorthand reporters who tested the Sholes-Glidden-Soule. So was the young lady who tricked Mark Twain. They were all hunt-and-peck devotees with individual typing styles who ordinarily used not more than a total of four fingers.

A daring spirit, Mrs. L. V. Longley of Cincinnati, proprietor of Longley's Shorthand and Typewriter Institute, was the first person on record with the audacity to propose that typists should use all the fingers of both hands. She wrote and published a pamphlet setting forth her incendiary ideas in 1882, and she had been teaching her students the method for some little time before she got it down on paper. Mrs. Longley's system was not a touch method. She was not concerned about where the typist kept his eyes. She simply thought it absurd to let four good fingers, the third and fourth of each hand, go to waste.

Conservative opinion felt that Mrs. Longley was off her rocker. As late as 1887, a trade magazine, the *Cosmopolitan Short-hander,* blasted away editorially at Mrs. Longley's radicalism and the hare-brained notions of the few who were following her lead:

> . . . Unless the third finger of the hand has been previously trained to touch the keys of a piano, we believe that it is not worth while to attempt to use that finger in operating the type-writer. The best operators we know of use only the first two fingers of each hand, and it is questionable whether a higher speed can be attained by the use of three.

Clearly, the writer felt that he had put down the foolish suggestion for the rest of time (except for pianists), and that the use of the fourth finger was too hopeless to condemn.

Mrs. Longley might have lost the argument if another rebel,

The Fountain Pen Crowd Took a Glum View

Frank E. McGurrin of Salt Lake City, had not appeared on the typewriting scene. The rescue he effected was entirely accidental. He didn't know Mrs. Longley, and there is no evidence that he had ever read her pamphlet. McGurrin was the official stenographer for the Federal Court in Salt Lake, and a sensationally good typist. He had taught himself. He had worked out his own ten-finger system on a Remington Model 1 in a law office in Grand Rapids, Michigan, where he had formerly been a clerk. And he could really make that typewriter jump.

Not only did McGurrin use ten fingers. He had also memorized the keyboard, and he was able to write without looking at his hands at all, blindfolded, if necessary, relying on his sense of touch alone.

Naturally McGurrin was proud of what he could do. He had practiced hard. He was like a man who has learned to perform a one-hand stand; he had devoted hours to something which was, on its face, fantastic, if not actually impossible. He took time off from his job and began to give demonstrations of his wondrous ability, first to gasping audiences in Salt Lake City and later throughout the western cities. Despite a rather mild, amiable appearance, there was a certain streak of truculence in McGurrin's nature. He was positive that he was the fastest typist in the world, and whenever he heard of anyone who might be considered a contender for the title, McGurrin hurled his challenge. He was ready to take on all comers in a match race at any place, any time. And he was ready to bet a substantial sum of money that McGurrin would win.

Now Cincinnati had another typewriting teacher besides Mrs. Longley, a certain Louis Taub, who took a poor view of ten-fingered typists. He believed, like the editors of the *Cosmopolitan Shorthander,* that four fingers were plenty. Moreover, Taub thought that the Remington and Remington's shift for capital letters was outmoded by the Caligraph and Caligraph's double keyboard with its two keys per letter, one upper- and the other lower-case. Finally, Taub felt reasonably certain that he was the fastest typewriter operator in the world.

McGurrin reddened just above his high stiff collar. He challenged. Taub accepted. McGurrin agreed to travel to Cincinnati —anything rather than allow the taint on his reputation to stand. The race was to be in two parts: forty-five minutes of direct dictation and forty-five minutes of copying from an unfamiliar script, and the man with the larger combined total number of words would win. The stake was $500.

Never before in United States history had a duel been fought with typewriters, and the event stirred up an extraordinary amount of public interest. Both the Remington and Caligraph company officials were torn between anxiety and hope. Mrs. Longley was in a state.

McGurrin won easily, just as he had predicted, on July 25, 1888. He won both separate events in addition to the aggregate. Typists all over the country noticed an extraordinary feature of his triumph. He had actually gone faster working from copy than when he had taken dictation. He had kept his eyes glued to the test material, never losing his place, never looking at his hands. Poor Taub, on the other hand, could only take in an eyeful at a time. He had fallen farther and farther behind, wagging his head like a spectator at a tennis match as he turned from script to keyboard and back again to script.

McGurrin v. Taub was a curiously decisive battle. It was immediately clear to everyone, Taub especially, that a good four-finger man didn't stand a chance against a good ten-finger man. It was clear that a speed typist had to memorize the keyboard or else keep very quiet about saying he could copy faster than McGurrin. And it followed, from that, that the double keyboard was doomed because it was too big to negotiate by touch alone, a point that Caligraph unfortunately missed.

Before long the *Cosmopolitan Shorthander,* without a word of apology for the nasty things it had said about third fingers, was over in McGurrin's corner, editorially, where Mrs. Longley had been for six years. A few months later, in 1889, Bates Torrey, of Portland, Maine, in a pamphlet, "A Manual of Practical Typewriting," used the word "touch" to describe the system McGurrin used, the first time the ten-fingers-don't-watch-your-hands method had had a convenient name.

The speed of typing had been a major sales argument ever since 1873, but now it was something more. It was a new kind of sports event. Prior to McGurrin v. Taub, the friends of the typewriter had been content to say that that machine was "twice as fast" as the hand, meaning that it was possible to type at about sixty words a minute. After the battle, the maximum possible typewriter speed was an open question.

For the next thirty-five years typewriter speed contests held the public interest, and typewriter speed queens and kings were celebrities of a minor luminosity. Organized baseball, which began in about the same period, never worried seriously about the annual World's Typewriting Championships as a threat to the World Series gate. And, as a cold matter of fact, the reigning speed typist was less important, even at the height of the craze, around 1910, than the world's table-tennis champion (Hiroja Satoh of Japan) is today. Nevertheless, speed typing drew crowds and inspired hundreds of thousands of dollars' worth of free newspaper and magazine publicity and the speedsters themselves, at least, took it very seriously.

One aspect of McGurrin v. Taub was most disturbing: even the *loser* was a male. Men, in their smug way, may have been pleased with this fact, but it did not jibe at all well with a great deal that had been written about woman's natural affinity for the typewriter; her nimbleness, her dexterity, her natural grace, and all that sort of thing—which perhaps had been merely a backhanded way of saying that she wasn't much good for anything else. Nor did it help the sales argument that, if you bought a typewriter, a girl went with it as extra equipment. It began to look as if businessmen should have been hiring male typewriters instead, a reversal that could have killed off the infant industry just as it was getting nicely under way.

A book publisher, of all people, was directly responsible for finding the way out of this dangerous impasse. D. Appleton & Company had an encyclopedia on its fall, 1888, list. The firm wanted publicity. It wanted to let the encyclopedia-buying public know, in particular, that the work was right up to the minute and that, for accuracy's sake, expense had been no consideration. It devised the perfect stunt. It would hold a special contest to determine how fast a very fast typist could go and include the figure in the up-to-date article, under "T," on the Typewriter. Each of the major typewriter manufacturers, Remington, Caligraph and Hammond, was invited to compete.

Remington accepted the invitation—as did the others—and held a preliminary speed contest to see who should have the honor of representing the industry's oldest typewriter name. Good publicity in it, Remington figured.

A young lady, Miss Mae Orr, a mere child but the head of her own firm of public stenographers and typists with an office at 120 Broadway, entered Remington's pre-Appleton contest. Good publicity for her business in it, she figured. Like McGurrin, Orr was a touch typist and exceedingly fast. She had been busy with her typing service, however, and did not hear about the Remington preliminaries until the morning of the very day, so that she had no time to practice. She won anyhow, but not by much.

In the few days before the main Appleton event, Orr practiced hard, for she didn't want to let Remington or Orr's Typing Service down. She needn't have bothered. Orr did close to one hundred words a minute. The second best speed was around eighty.

The D. Appleton & Company editors were terribly embarrassed. They knew that a very fast typist could do eighty wpm, for dozens had done so. But there was Orr, in a class by herself, ridiculously far ahead of all the others. They didn't know what to say. They didn't want the article in the encyclopedia to look like a Remington-Orr house ad. They weren't entirely sure that Orr was not a freak. So, to be on the safe, accurate side, they omitted the whole bothersome sentence.

Nevertheless Orr, whose fingers were by now well loosened up, decided to challenge McGurrin. McGurrin came storming to New York in August and, to the dismay of all those devoted to woman's emancipation, battled Orr down. He beat her by three-fifths of a word, 95⅘ to 95⅕, but there were those among the spectators who felt that McGurrin had frightened Orr into defeat. Orr had actually gone faster than McGurrin, but she had made a lot more mistakes. It was only on net speed, after a deduction for errors, that the brute had triumphed. At Toronto, two weeks later, in a return match, Orr seemed more calm. Her fingers fairly flew. She made mistakes. But her net speed was 98.7, several words per minute better than McGurrin had been able to do. The second sex, as far as typewriting was concerned, was first.

Another great lady champion, probably the greatest of all time, emerged in 1905. Her name was Rose Fritz. Speed typing had been rather informal between 1888 and 1905, with lots of challenge matches and lots of exhibitions, but no satisfactorily clear-cut national championship to settle the conflicting boasts of various contenders. In 1906, the trade magazine *Office Appliances* put up a beautiful trophy. It was to become the permanent property of anyone who won it three consecutive times, which seemed well-nigh impossible at the time, for the landscape was dotted with first-class competitors. The donors had not figured on Miss Fritz. She retired the cup in her first three tries with winning speeds of sixty-four, eighty-two and eighty-four net words per minute, which sounds as if speed writing had gotten less speedy since 1888, but was actually a reflection of the very severe stiffening of the rules. *Office Appliances*, with the help of donations from most of the typewriter manufacturers, put up an even bigger, fancier cup. Miss Fritz won, for the fourth consecutive time, in 1907. And again in 1908. And again in 1909, with a net of ninety-five words per minute. Whereupon Miss Fritz, tucking both her trophies under her arm, retired from championship competition, undefeated and unparalleled, and let a mere man, H. O. Blaisdell, who had been finishing second to Fritz with dogged regularity, capture the crown in 1910.

Both Fritz and Blaisdell raced on Underwoods, and by the time they had chalked up eight consecutive victories between them all the other typewriter manufacturers were fed up with speed championships. So were the business-machines manufacturers in general. At first they had loved the contests, held in conjunction with their annual office-equipment show, because lots of people turned out to watch Rose Fritz's dazzling speed; but the public had grown so interested in typewriting racing

---

Prize Winners in a Typewriting Speed Content

Stella Willins, 1926 Amateur Champion, Visited Birmingham, England, on an Exhibition Tour

that it was ignoring exhibits of stuff like adding machines and file cabinets, the real point of the exposition. Before long the typing championships were banished to another city. If the business-equipment exposition was held in New York, for instance, the typewriter races were in Boston, or vice versa, but still simultaneously, for the publicity value of the speedsters was irreplaceable, and desirable, too, as long as the typewriter racing didn't steal the entire spotlight.

In 1915 Underwood typists were still winning, to the growing pique of the other firms, and to Underwood's unconcealed de-

light. It was the long Underwood dominance of the championships, more than anything else, that finally killed the sport, for
finally no other company wanted to play. The Underwood
Model 5, the machine of champions, was fast, but no faster than
Royal, Remington or L. C. Smith, to name a few. All speed
typists realized that a champion like Rose Fritz, for instance,
would have won on any old typewriter, and that in typewriter
racing, unlike horse racing, the jockey is practically everything.
The point had been proven repeatedly, because several speed
kings and queens *had* switched from one company's stable to
another's, and it had had no appreciable effect on their speed.
But the man in the street didn't know that. He couldn't help
thinking that Underwood, since it always took the speed title,
must be faster than other typewriters, as Underwood advertising confidently proclaimed.

Underwood did have something no other company had. It
was a genius named Charles E. Smith. He was the coach of the
Underwood racing stable of speed kings and queens, its talent
scout, and the inventor of a set of special speed-typing techniques. Year after year Smith thought up some improvement in
racing form and taught it to his protégés, and unless a com-
petitor had the latest Smith secret he hardly had a chance. One
did not learn Smith's new tricks, needless to say, unless one had
joined the Underwood team.

Besides his ingenuity, Smith had a great eye for talent. He
haunted all the major secretarial schools in and around New
York City, keeping his eyes peeled for kids who looked like
potential champions. He spotted Stella Willins, for instance,
who became the world's amateur title-holder in 1926, when she
had finished only two and a half months of a six months' beginning secretarial course. Whenever Smith found promising talent, he snapped it up for Underwood. He offered a job at an
excellent starting typist's salary. Instead of struggling with some

dull executive's dictation, the boy or girl got to join Smith's glamorous squad of famous racing typists, known formally as the Underwood Speed Training Group. The squad worked hard. A huge, loftlike room in a building at 30 Vesey Street was its gymnasium, and the purr of typewriters doing one hundred words a minute and better filled the air eight hours a day, five days a week. Each typist had his own racing typewriter, an Underwood, naturally, and never let anybody borrow it, or thought of using another, for it was custom adjusted to suit his fingers. He carried it to matches, or on exhibition tours, in a big, plush-lined case with wardrobe-trunk-type latches and special protective fittings to guard against accidental bumps or jars, and he worried about it the way a concert violinist worries about a Stradivarius, holding the huge thing on his lap, if necessary, rather than letting it be consigned to a baggage car. The machines were stock models but souped up, like a hot-rod racing automobile, almost beyond recognition, especially their escapements, the many-toothed wheels which controlled their carriages, which had been filed to hair-trigger delicacy; they'd let the carriage move on to the next space if anybody gave them so much as a sharp look. It was extraordinarily generous of the Underwood Company, considering how much money it put into winning, not to demand that the speedsters use shiny new machines which would look good in the news photographs, but to let them race with the well-worn, battered, frightful-looking Underwoods they loved.

The training at 30 Vesey Street was almost continuous, but its pace accelerated about four months before the annual World Championships, when Smith began to point his squad for the big pay-off test. He tried, like a prize fighter's trainer, to get the racing typists in peak condition on the day of the matches, and not earlier, if it could be avoided, for fear that they might go stale. The difference between Smith and a fight trainer was that

Smith had to cope with, not one, but as many as twenty athletes in three different classes, professionals, amateurs (meaning salaried typists who had not won a major title) and novices (who had studied for less than twelve months). He had to help the champion defend successfully and, at the same time, spur on the leading contender. His job, besides everything else, required a flair for diplomacy of the highest order. He was a soft-spoken man, full of enthusiasm and fire, and at the same time extremely dignified. Smith's austere good manners, more than anything else, enabled him to teach everybody without letting anybody feel slighted. He kept the entire squad working in the big Vesey Street room, rather than break it up into several more easily manageable groups, for good reasons. Any given speedster, in any given class, could tell immediately whether or not he or she was up to speed simply by comparing the rattle of his own keys with the champion's typing rhythm, an automatic check that not only served as a constant inspiration but saved a lot of stopwatch timing, counting and computing. As long as Smith and the entire squad were in plain sight of each other, furthermore, no one could suspect him of teaching favorites some extra little something. The three reigning champions, as of any given moment, liked the arrangement as well as the least experienced novice. Novices, of course, were thrilled to train in immediate proximity to internationally known celebrities who had had their pictures in all the papers, whose testimonials had been featured in advertising layouts, and who had traveled, on expense accounts, all over the world, or at least to those parts of the world included in the Underwood export scheme. Title-holders, for their part, liked to know that all their leading rivals were collected at 30 Vesey Street where they could be watched. There was no serious thought that anyone outside Smith's squad, training in secret by himself, had a chance to score an upset.

Despite Smith's fairness, however, the big family of young

men and women was not entirely happy. The competition was fierce. The championship contests themselves may have degenerated into little more than Underwood parties, as the other typewriter firms said, but the champions and the would-be champions were fighting just as hard as possible, and the strain was almost more than could be borne, for the speed standards kept going up as Smith devised one split-second-saving technique after another. The inevitable inter-squad feuds and cliques developed. Insults and tears were not unknown. Sometimes two speedsters would not speak to each other for weeks, even though their typewriters were only a few feet apart. Yet it was imperative for a racer to keep calm, sleep well and avoid emotional distress. For otherwise, when he reached one of the dreaded plateaus in training, in which he could not go any faster or even slipped back a notch or two, he might crack up completely.

Squad members were always under the pressure of having to revise their styles, because Smith was constantly thinking of something new, and one hardly dared race without it. One of Smith's inventions, for example, was the speed paper insert. It was as important to a championship typist as the pool turn is to an Olympic free-style swimmer, for the change from one sheet of the prescribed legal-size typewriter racing paper to the next was a critical moment. A fumbler might lose as much as a full second, and at a speed of, say, 115 words per minute the problem arose every four minutes or so, since there were thirty-five thirteen-word lines to the page, about 455 words in all. Some amateur typists think they have done well if they get a new sheet of paper in straight on the first try without dropping anything on the floor, and the time consumed is not a serious consideration. The speed squad was compelled to take quite a different view. After Smith had invented his paper-change method, the right-hand carriage draw (as opposed to the left-hand carriage throw), no one had much chance of winning unless he could remove the typed sheet and insert a clean one *while the carriage was in motion returning from left to right.*

As soon as the last word on the last line had been typed, the racer took hold of the right-hand roller knob with the second, third and fourth fingers of the right hand, at the same time hooking onto the paper holder with the index finger, pulling the carriage from left to right and rotating the roller simultaneously. The typed sheet popped up and fell onto the table behind the machine. It had not been touched at all. Meanwhile the left hand had reached down to the paper supply, immediately to the left of the typewriter. The pile, arranged in advance, was neatly staggered, sheet by sheet, so that the left hand could pick up a single piece of paper without an instant's groping, and yet the stack was as compact as possible, so that the left hand wouldn't lose time by having to reach farther than absolutely necessary. As soon as the old sheet had cleared the roller, the new sheet was ready to start into the paper feed. As soon as the new sheet had engaged the paper feed and main rollers, the left hand was on its way back to normal typing position. By the time the carriage had stopped moving, the new paper was in position and both hands were back in motion. The typist accomplished all this without looking away from the copy and in perhaps one-third of a second, so fast that it hardly broke the typing rhythm.

In addition to the strain of learning new techniques as fast as Smith invented them, the young men and women had to struggle to combine stamina with speed, for the championship professional course was a full hour's run. The racers had to build up endurance, and had to learn to pace themselves like mile runners. As long as a typist was making steady progress he was not likely to worry, but inevitably he'd come to a morale-shattering point of no advance. It was enough to drive him crazy, especially if his closest adversary happened to be going great guns at the time. A day off would sometimes help him through the doldrums. Or a double dose of finger-breaking effort might do the trick. One champ found that she could often break through such a barrier and go on to new heights if she finished off her training day, normally devoted to long-sustained endurance drills, with a wild, almost hysterical, thirty-second burst of super-speed as a kind of dessert. More often than not, by the next day she'd find that some of the speed gained in her carefree frenzies had been carried over to her controlled, full-route pace.

The tension in the air at 30 Vesey Street mounted as the championships approached. The matches were usually held at night. The old Madison Square Garden at Madison Avenue and Twenty-sixth Street was often the scene. During those years when the races were part of the business show, they were held on the second floor, on a level above the main exhibits, in a small, square arena formed by wooden grandstands and brilliantly lit with batteries of overhead floodlights. There were always quite a few contestants besides the members of Smith's squad—just as there are tennis players who have not been brought up in Southern California under Perry Jones's direction who enter the National Singles Tournament at Forest Hills—so that there were some machines in action besides Underwoods. Most of these outsiders simply did not realize what they were up against.

Racing was by class, with all the entrants in the amateur division, for instance, working simultaneously on identical copy. There was quite a flurry of activity immediately before the starting bell. Typewriters were unpacked. Keyboard heights, usually around twenty-nine inches from the floor, were brought to fine adjustment by slipping wooden blocks of varying thicknesses under the typewriters' feet. Stationery was stacked in racing array. There was considerable sitting down, getting up and wriggling around, for it was essential to start in an entirely comfortable position, just as it was essential for the girls to wear loose, simple sports dresses without any unnecessary frills or baubles. (Golf dresses, with plenty of shoulder room for free arm movement, were especially popular.) The men, as usual, wore ordinary shirts and trousers. Racers of both sexes used special racing typists' visors, long-beaked affairs covered in green cloth with their edges turned down sharply on both sides for about three inches. They cut off any glare from the overhead lights and, at the same time, acted like blinders on a race horse; once the typist's eyes were fixed on the copy he couldn't see anything else to right or left.

Finally the bell sounded, and they were off!

It is hard to imagine how fast a typist goes to net, say, 120 words per minute unless you have seen a championship performance. A very good non-racing office stenographer may gross eighty words per minute, and she sounds fast. Championship speed was nearly twice that fast. In order to net 120, a racer actually typed at least 140, for each error meant a ten-word deduction, and the definitions of errors were tough. If a contestant wrote more than seventy-six or less than sixty-one letters in a line, that was counted a mistake. If a letter was not entirely legible, that was a mistake. If a letter failed to strike exactly in the middle of its space, or if the margin was not perfectly even, or if the escapement jumped a space, those were all errors; not to mention garden-variety mistakes, of course, like hitting the wrong letter, transposing, missing a word, or misspelling.

A word was arbitrarily defined as having five strokes, so that a gross of 120 meant six hundred strokes a minute or ten strokes a second, as fast as a fast piano trill where the pianist merely hits adjacent keys. Stella Willins once wrote 264 words in one

Albert Tangora Completing a Racing Paper Change

minute (repeating a memorized sentence). That is twenty-two finger strokes per second, a more reasonable speed for reading than for writing.

There was very little noise in the racing arena except the loud purring of the machines—not that noise would have bothered the racers, for their concentration was far too intense. They were entirely unaware of the crowds, once they were under way, and, in fact, they were not too well aware of anything, including the sense of what they were copying. The Smith gang brought their fight with them from the Vesey Street gymnasium. The race proper became an almost mechanical process. Their fingers hit the right keys as a matter of conditioned-reflex action. The

ideal state of mind—after so many days of tension—was a kind
of slap-happy, passive calm. The slightest trace of self-conscious-
ness was a fatal drawback. Pianists and violinists have spoken
about this same phenomenon. They were so nervous, they have
said, that they didn't realize what they were doing until after
the first intermission; the concert was in their fingers and they
had simply let themselves go. The racing typists, at their best,
did the same thing. Which is not to say that there was no effort
in their performances. The exertion was tremendous. After an
hour's race, the floor around each typist's chair was literally wet
from the perspiration that had dripped down his arms and off
his elbows.

An ideal spectator sport needs a clear-cut, obvious denou-
ment—a knockout, a touchdown, a home run, or something
equivalent. Typewriter racing had no dramatic climax and this,
as much as Smith's strangle hold on the sport, may have been its
downfall. When the bell for the finish had sounded and the
messy piles of papers in back of the typewriters had been picked
up, it took the judges a discouragingly long time to announce
the winner, for they had to correct, often using magnifying
glasses on questions of spacing and legibility, count, subtract
and then do the whole thing over a couple of times to be sure
they were right. Lots of the fans went home and to bed before
the new champion was crowned, figuring it was simpler to wait
and read all about it in the next morning's papers.

The end came with a whimper rather than a bang. Typewriter
races by the hundreds are still held every year, but they are
small-fry stuff by comparison with the Golden Era, mostly for
novices and local in scope. Some great racers are still around
and still in excellent form, notably Albert Tangora, a professional who does exhibitions wearing the Royal colors, holder of
the world's record of a net 142 five-stroke words per minute set
in Chicago in 1941 using a Royal standard. (Tangora doesn't

mention the fact—unless he is asked directly—that Smith trained him to race on the Underwood, and that in 1923, before the five-stroke definition of a word had been adopted, he did 147 net actual words per minute on his Underwood Model 5.) It is barely possible that speed-typing contests may have a revival. But the chances are heavily against it. And for one dominant reason: all standard typewriters are a whole lot faster than typists. And Smith's squad showed, to almost everyone's satisfaction, how fast typists can be.

9 / No Longer Funny

About 1915 vaudeville comedians discovered that they could no longer get away with jokes about typewriters. ("I saw you and your queen walking down Main Street last night." "Oh, that was not my queen. That was my typewriter!")

As late as 1911 it had been possible to get a laugh, or at least a snicker, with: "Wanna see something? Well, all you have to do is hit the key next to Z and you can see the X raise. X-Rays!"

But by 1915, a bad year for vaudeville in general, the typewriter gag was dead. The Ford automobile was funny. The popular song, "The Love Story of the Packard and the Ford," was funny. Charlie Chaplin was hilarious, and vaudeville houses were holding contests to see which local amateur could imitate him best.

But the typewriter had become a commonplace and had stopped being funny. Every business firm in the country was typewriting its correspondence and keeping typewritten records, with the exception of a handful that felt they could achieve some sort of swank by being outrageously old-fashioned. The

131

Gus Edwards' "Six Blonde Typewriters" Tapped Out Type-
writer Rhythm Accompaniments for Songs and Dances

"curiosity-breeding little joker" had lost its provocative quality.

Among the many signs that the typewriter had passed ado-
lescence and reached a kind of maturity was the fact that a
whole host of other business machines and office gadgets depended upon it.

Some, like ribbons, carbons, erasers, ink eradicators, type-
and platen-cleaning fluids, were actually typewriter supplies.

Others, like dictating and transcribing machines, typewriter
desks, typewriter stands, typists' posture chairs, and duplicating
machines, while a short step farther removed, were produced
on the firm assumption that typewriters were here to stay.

Businesses that had been in existence before typewriters, like
file-cabinet and stationery manufacturing, had undergone a
revolution brought on by the typewriter, and dreaded to think
what would happen if, for any reason, the device were abolished.

Accounting machines, adding machines, addressing machines,
billing machines, calculating machines, cash registers, check-
writing machines, and the entire printing industry, via the Linotype, depended on the typewriter in the sense that they incor-

porated a typewriterlike mechanism within themselves and were offshoots of the typewriter.

Not to forget the service and repair businesses, which depended on the fact that the typewriter not only existed but, from time to time, broke down.

Including families and relatives, it added up to quite a few persons who would not laugh, unless nervously, if a Keith-Orpheum Circuit comic made fun of writing machines.

Alert students of the American language, furthermore, had begun to detect typewriter influences, a reliable indication that the machine had attained major status. In pre-typewriter days businessmen had evolved a complicated set of labor- and ink-saving contractions and abbreviations which they combined with euphuisms and clichés that were wasteful but gave the impression, to many, that the author was a big operator; "Yrs of the 12 inst rec'd and contents duly noted," for instance, when any fool would know that there'd be no answer if the original communication had gone astray.

A man unfamiliar with the jargon could hardly read it.

No one talked the language of business correspondence. It was entirely a written phenomenon. Business schools of the pre-typewriter era taught their pupils, along with shorthand, or phonography, as it was generally called, how to read and write business English without losing too much in the translation. Even after the typewriter had arrived, adding enormously to the popularity of dictating as a way of writing, there was considerable clinging to the old forms out of habit. But gradually the abbreviations disappeared. Unfortunately the flowery or roundabout phrase stayed. It was hard to dictate in a terse, precise fashion. Words came easily. Businessmen, relieved from having to trace out the letters with their own fingers, and saved from the dangers of ink blots, stains and splatters, fell into all sorts of evil practices, particularly the sin of starting a sentence without a plan for finishing it. ("We are pleased to forward to you the merchandise referred to in your valued order of the 21st except that, on account of unforeseen difficulties in the supply of materials, we have substituted light blue for navy hoping that this will not inconvenience you rather than cause further delay which, as you know, we are as anxious to avoid as you are in view of our pleasure during these past months of being of service to your esteemed organization as well as personally.")

In 1904, in an *Atlantic Monthly* article, Robert Lincoln O'Brien, who was among the first to comment on the subject, wrote:

> The invention of the typewriter has given a tremendous impetus to the dictating habit. . . . This means not only greater diffuseness, inevitable with any lessening of the tax on words which the labor of writing imposes, but it also brings forward the point of view of the one who speaks. There is the disposition on the part of the talker to explain, as if watching the facial expressions of his hearers to see how far they are following. This attitude is not lost when his audience becomes merely a clicking typewriter. It is no uncommon thing in the typewriting booths at the Capitol in Washington to see Congressmen in dictating letters use the most vigorous gestures as if the oratorical methods of persuasion could be transmitted to the printed page. . . .

All writers, not just businessmen, senators and representatives, were affected.

The dictation habit raised the possibility that a letter writer might never see the letter he had written. When he had not, a notation, "Dictated but not signed," was considered the stylish way to show that his signature, if any, was a rubber stamp or a forgery perpetrated by his secretary. It was popular right after World War I, and it is still used. It implied that the letter writer

Her Master's Voice on the Dictaphone

was such a busy fellow that he didn't have time to squiggle his mark on his correspondence. And it gave businessmen a new freedom; they could say any old thing and, if called to the mat later on, claim that their girl had heard wrong or had lost a couple of key words in a crack in the wax Dictaphone cylinder.

It had other forms: "Dictated but not read," and, better still, "Dictated but not read and not signed." Only recently did it reach full flower. It has become, as it is currently used by really big tycoons: "Dictated by transatlantic telephone and recorded on tape, but not read and not signed."

Some of the influences of the typewriter on English composition were all to the good, however. Teachers had noticed, early in the game, that the clarity of machine writing forced people to improve their spelling and punctuation. The penman, in doubt about whether the "i" should precede the "e," had usually written an ambiguous "ie" that could be taken for "ei." Or had made the entire word a snakelike ripple that could be understood only from context.

Typewriting brought things out in the open. Dictionary sales zoomed, and persons who had never before given the semicolon any serious thought began to use it on the slightest excuse. There were still those wretches who, confronted by the "e" and "i" dilemma, resorted to the low dodge of typing "e," backspacing, and then hitting the "i" on top of it. But, for the most part, good typists were good at spelling and skillful in the use of punctuation, if only because it saved erasing.

One of the earliest of the typewriter gags, indirectly, had referred to the point:

BOSS: Can you spell?

TYPEWRITER: Not very well, I'm afraid.

BOSS: I'm sorry, then, you won't do. You see, I can't spell either.

Typewriting became a subdivision of the science of educational psychology, which was a third proof that it amounted to something. The subdivision was itself divided in two. There was the science of teaching men and women to typewrite, and, secondly, the technique of using typewriters to teach boys and girls to read, and to write by hand. Educators seldom convened at

Atlantic City without discussing one or the other or both of these matters.

Teaching by typewriter is a particularly intriguing form of pedagogy. The theory and practice, stripped of academic terminology, is this:

When parents discover, as they often do, that their child is almost old enough to manage a paper route but has not yet learned the first two of his three "R"s, and if the parents are sophisticated enough to know that beatings are only likely to stir up all sorts of formidable psychological resistances, an ordinary typewriter offers them a marvelous weapon.

For if they will leave the machine lying around the house in a conspicuous place, sooner or later the child is attracted to it, especially if he has been told that it is Daddy's typewriter and an object to be left entirely alone. The illiterate, after circling the machine suspiciously a few times, darts at it suddenly and, in imitation of what he has seen Daddy doing, strikes a few keys. Ordinarily he produces something like "sdmK r7bn%m" and a good many proud parents file the copy as a souvenir. But the child can seldom be satisfied until he has been told that he really hasn't written much. "Why not?" is his next question. At this point the parents explain just a little bit about writing, making it plain that they don't care whether the child listens or not.

Invariably the child demands to be allowed to type his own name, which means that he has to learn how to spell it, and that he has to notice that the various letters have various formations because that's the easiest way of identifying the proper keys. If the child has a good long name like Christopher, for instance, he may learn as much as $^{10}/_{26}$ of the entire alphabet in one sitting, and at no one's insistence but his own.

It really works.

It does sound, at first blush, like a trick a typewriter salesman might have invented trying to insure maximum wear and tear on the machine and hoping he'd be there to close a deal on a replacement. It was actually a phenomenon spotted by educational experts and described by men like Dr. Benjamin D. Wood of Columbia and Dr. F. N. Freeman of the University of Chicago, whose book, *An Experimental Study of the Educational Influences of the Typewriter in the Elementary School Classroom,* appeared in 1923. For a good many years, now, any elementary school with any interest in being thought up-to-date has had at least a couple of battered typewriters dedicated to this form of learning-by-doing. According to the best psychological doctrines, infant typists are not to be given more than the most elementary instruction in typing *per se.* It is okay to tell a kindergartner that the idea of the machine, basically, is to push down the key corresponding to the letter desired. And if, in an exceptional case, one is confronted by a John Stuart Mill-type prodigy who wants to know how to spell "ratiocination," he can be told. But with the normal baby, one teaches nothing at all about good typing technique, for if the child realizes that typing is in itself a subject to be studied, as repulsive as rhythms or group play, the whole thing is likely to turn sour. Somewhere around the sixth grade, the two aspects of typewriter pedagogy achieve a blend, and the typewriter, formerly a substitute teacher, becomes a part of the curriculum. Comparatively few sixth-graders are actually studying typing at this moment, but the average age of student typists gets lower every year. Most high schools teach it, and have been doing so for decades. A great many junior high schools are also doing so, and their number is rapidly increasing.

Shortly after the typewriter appeared, one gloomy prophet, writing anonymously in a stenographers' trade journal, predicted that it would mean the end of man's ability to write in his own hand. His fear was groundless. Some of 1954's teen-agers do write atrociously, but so did some of 1874's. If handwriting has reached a low state, the typewriter cannot be blamed. For the experts' researches show that familiarity with typewriting makes students better penmen, not worse. The typewritten word seems to set a standard for neatness. The letters are not quite the same as handwritten letters, to be sure, but the "o"s are round, the "t"s are crossed, and the "i"s are dotted. And the straightness of the lines (unless the machine is in desperately poor shape) can hardly be beaten. Typewriting teaches a lesson, and nobody has to say a word to make the point: even handwriting should be legible.

Close to three million persons, right now, are studying typing in a formal manner. Goodness knows how many others may be teaching themselves, perhaps with the help of one of the dozens of good instruction books like *20th Century Typewriting* by

The Touch System Takes Practice

Lessenberry-Crawford (Southwestern Publishing Company) or *Gregg Typing—New Series* by Rowe-Lloyd (McGraw Hill).

There are twenty-three thousand schools, including high schools, teaching typing, and there are seven hundred thousand practice typewriters used for four periods a day, on the average.

Typing students in 1915 were clickity-clacking away at the boring drills for vocational reasons, and the situation has not changed. Most of the current crop of students figure it means a job. Most of them are right—and how many Latin scholars can make the same rationalization?

Yet at the same time, several of the most fashionable prep schools in the country—whose male students are concentrating, primarily, on the difficult subject of learning to behave like young gentlemen, and who expect to dictate, for the most part, rather than transcribe—are teaching typing with a frenzy at least equal to any High School of Commerce. For typing is considered a social grace, as well as a skill that can be exchanged for wages.

The science of expert typing is an impressive affair, as anyone who has been to a secretarial school is well aware. A few controversies divide the experts in the field, like the debate over whether, in beginning exercises, it is preferable for the student to maintain keyboard orientation in horizontal-line terms, coming back always to the "home" or "asdfghjkl" line, or to think vertically, in terms of the keys each of his fingers covers, and it is pretty hard to say that truth lies entirely on one side of the argument. In any case, almost everybody agrees what a good typist does:

She sits erect in a comfortable position, with her feet flat on the floor and her arms relaxed. Her typewriter table and her chair are of such heights that her arms slope slightly downward, from wrists to elbows, paralleling the slope of the keyboard. Her elbows are in, her wrists are rather low; her fingers are curved and close to the "home" keys. She strokes the keys firmly, using finger action entirely. Her arms and wrists are motionless.

Her eyes are on the copy. She doesn't look for line endings; she waits until the ping of the bell tells her the right-hand margin is near. She returns to the next line as soon as possible after the bell has sounded for the next round, and she *throws* the carriage, a hefty sock, holding the fingers of the left hand almost flat and close together, striking the carriage-return lever with the second joint of the index finger.

By the time the carriage has bumped into position, her hands are back in regular position on the keyboard. She resumes typing instantly, picking up the smooth rhythm of her work almost without interruption—or, at most, after losing not more than one beat.

She is fast and accurate; she does at least sixty words a minute, and, at that pace, she can transcribe three thousand words without more than two or three errors. (Speed and accuracy are not enemies; they go together. A good typist is likely to make fewer mistakes at her top cruising speed than if she slowed down to a snail's pace, trying to avoid an error at all costs.)

She looks at the actual word in the copy that she is transcribing. She doesn't read ahead, and she doesn't look back at the machine to see how she is doing. She concentrates on the sense of what she is copying. She makes her job look absurdly easy.

She has mastered a galaxy of separate techniques before she can whang out one perfect word after another at a rate of one per second. She knows shorthand so well that she doesn't have to peer at her notes trying to figure them out, for that would destroy typing continuity. The mechanics of her typewriter are entirely familiar. Her desk is systematically organized, and she can handle the difficult items like carbons and ribbons with surgeonlike dexterity.

When she makes a mistake, she gets out of the blunder with

finesse. It has often been said that Gene Sarazen, golf champion, is so expert at getting out of sand traps that he aims for them. Sarazen himself denies it, and no first-class stenographer tries for typing mistakes just because she's good at erasing. But a good typist, like Sarazen, is not ridden with fears about making mistakes. She *can* recover, and beautifully, if she has to.

Her first thought is: How *little* can I erase?

Some letters can be struck over, if the error is not too black, without any erasure at all. If she has hit "c" lightly, for example, and she should have hit "o," she can simply backspace and print "o" over the "c" and hardly anyone will be one whit the wiser; or "e" can be struck over "c" without trouble.

And there are a great many letters that *almost* fit one on top of the other.

If she has hit "e," meaning to hit "s," she needn't try to erase the top and bottom curves or the middle cross-bar of the "e"; all she has to do is get rid of the right and left sides, a comparatively minor matter. Or, if she has hit "i" instead of "t" she needs to erase only the left-hand projection of its foot, for "t" covers up all the rest of "i."

Having determined the minimum amount of erasing she'll have to do, she moves the carriage to the right or left, far enough to clear the paper fingers and the writing scale and to avoid dropping eraser crumbs into the type basket, and, using an eraser shield to keep fingerprints off the page, she erases with short, light downward strokes. She never rubs back and forth as if she had a saw in hand. She strokes in one direction, lifting the eraser at the end of each stroke so that she can see how she is doing.

When the erasure is done, she returns to the printing space and taps the correct letter with the lightest possible touch. She may, for the first blow—to make sure that the paper has not slipped or gotten out of alignment—shift the ribbon onto stencil, so that it will make a very subtle, inkless impression and nothing more. Then, seeing that the spacing is as it should be, she taps the correction up to matching darkness with two or three light taps.

Above all, the mark of good typing is a continuous, even rhythm. An expert keeps going. She can complete a letter—barring an error and erasure—without looking at her machine at all. She does everything by touch, including the margin-release, the tabulator, and unusual characters, like @ and %.

No one has ever studied typewriting without worrying about the arrangement of the keys. And for good reason.

The standard keyboard—standard in the sense of uniform on English-language typewriters—makes practically no sense at all.

It is all Sholes's fault. There is no positive explanation for what he did. He did *not* follow the arrangement of the printer's type case, as has been written time and time again; that is pure legend. Sholes, according to his friend and associate, Dr. Roby, first set the keys in alphabetical order. Certainly there are vestiges of it, especially across the middle row: "fghjkl," for example, with the missing "i," on the line above, not so far out of place. But as Sholes struggled through one model after another he constantly changed the keyboard order, trying to avoid certain collisions and jamming that cropped up. By the time Densmore and Yost were ready to sell the Sholes experimental machine to Philo Remington, it had gotten to:

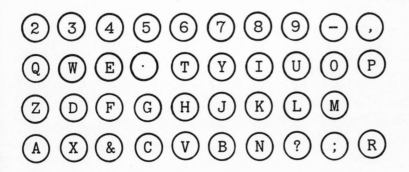

And a few months later, after the Remington mechanics had had a go at improving things, it was:

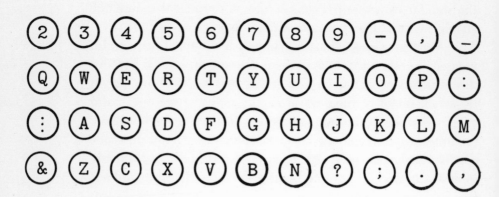

Which is very close to what we've got now, the main difference being the transposed "C" and "X" and the addition of characters made possible by the invention of the shift:

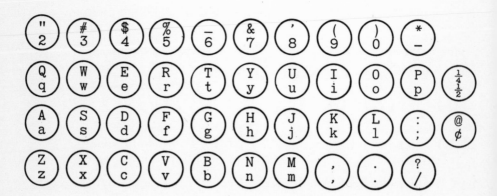

Judged scientifically, however, from the standpoint of the touch typist, this arrangement of the alphabet is madly inconvenient. According to one of the many persons, including psychologists, engineers and student Ph.D.'s, who have studied it, the standard keyboard is considerably less efficient than if the arrangement had been left to simple chance.

In the first place, it is left-handed. Most typists are right-handed, and their right hands are more agile than their left. But the standard order, sometimes called the "querty uiop," gives the left hand 56 per cent of the total number of strokes. It also gives weak fingers, particularly the little finger of the left hand, too much work, including the two toughest keys, the shift-lock and the back-spacer. In the third place it demands an entirely unnecessary amount of awkward reaching because it ignores the frequency with which the letters of the alphabet are encountered, which is, in order: E T A O S I N R H L D C U M Y B P W F G V K J X Q Z. It should bunch the most common, of course. A rational keyboard would try to make the most of what's easiest, which is hitting a letter with one hand and the next with the other hand. A word like "federated," for instance, is a terror. On the query uiop keyboard, the left hand does it all; the right hand runs some danger of muscular atrophy while it waits for the left hand to finish. Whereas a word like "sicken" is a cinch, for it employs first the left and then the right and then the left again, flip flap flip, flap flip flap. Forty-eight per cent of all finger motions on the standard are one-handed, the hard way. On a sensible keyboard they shouldn't amount to more than 33 per cent.

Among one-handed motions, hurdles—in which the finger has to jump a key to get from here to there—are the most difficult. It's bad enough to move from "f" to "r," but it's worse to jump from "v" to "r" over the top of "f." (The hurdle from "z" to "q" with the little finger of the left hand is the nadir, but fortunately

it almost never comes up.) If you wanted to write something
about an extremely small, or minimum pumpkin, you'd be in
serious typing difficulty. The two words keep the right hand
jumping like a wild grasshopper. On the standard keyboard 11
per cent of all motions are hurdles. They could be cut to 1 per
cent.

In short, a pretty mess of keys. Dozens of sensible reform
keyboards have been invented by people like the late Roy T.
Griffith, a telephone-company engineer, and Dr. Roy Hoke of
Johns Hopkins. Nearly all of them incorporate similar ideas: let
each finger work according to its ability, and let the most common combinations of letters be the easiest. Hoke's proposal is
among the most radical. He proposes to make the index fingers
operate the back-space, shift and shift-lock, because index fingers are strongest. And so he moves those three keys in from the
outer fringes of the keyboard to the very center, in addition to
shuffling the letters around. Like this:

His "home" line, the "rnthu sieoa" line, you'll notice, contains the nine most-used letters. And five out of the first six are

in the right hand. Hoke's reformed keyboard is one of the best, if not the best, but lots of the others are good, too.

Almost any reasonable man, upon realizing that the typewriter keyboard is silly, would ask, "Why doesn't somebody do something about it?" He might even nominate himself as the reformer, thinking that a machine with a superior key arrangement ought to make a lot of money.

Before you invest any of your savings in a keyboard-reform scheme, consider the sad facts.

If the public would buy it, Royal, Remington, Smith-Corona, Underwood and IBM would all be selling it.

Quite a few persons have already lost quite a lot of money for their failure to realize this. Mechanically speaking, any of the typewriter firms can arrange the keys in any order quite easily. Minor rearrangements, on special order, are a matter of routine. Nothing to it.

They cannot rearrange the querty uiop keyboard because millions of buyers know how to typewrite by touch on it and don't want to learn a different system. Typing, after reform, would be easier and faster, it's true. But not enough easier and not enough faster to justify the havoc.

From very early in typewriter history, the idea of changing Sholes's nonsensical keyboard has been hopeless. Typist opinion was against the change, even when there were very few typists, and even before touch dominated the scene.

A few firms, Hammond among them, tried to hold out against the querty uiop, feeling that virtue should in the long run be rewarded. All of the companies that tried to prove that a more sensible key order was more sensible have long since departed.

Not so very long ago, one of the world's greatest corporations, not a typewriter concern but a manufacturer of almost everything else in the world, got all steamed up about typewriter-keyboard improvement. Patents were purchased. Studies were made. Special operators were hired to unlearn the querty uiop and learn the new keyboard. Tests were made. Sure enough, the improved keyboard worked beautifully.

But the typewriter buyers of the country said to the giant corporation, in effect, "It's lovely. It works better than anything else. And you can keep it." In the end there was nothing but lots of ugly red ink in the ledgers to mark the noble experiment.

There was a fourth indication that the typewriter had come to stay: it was providing gainful employment—or, at least, amusement—to several fascinating and highly special kinds of specialists.

The typewriter detective was one. Not the detective mentioned earlier, who specialized in recovering stolen machines. But the specialist in identifying samples of typewriting as the product of a given machine, on the theory, which has considerable validity, that every typewriter, like every human thumb or canine nose, makes its own unique impression.

Conan Doyle was among the first to capitalize on the notion. He wrote a Sherlock Holmes story, "A Case of Identity," copyright 1892, which turned on the identification by typewriter of a certain impostor, thus making the Woodstock of Hiss case fame, more than a half century later, look like pretty old stuff. By the second decade of the twentieth century, a number of such typewriting-identification experts were set up in business. Their main job was legal work. Like handwriting experts (and in several cases, the typewriting experts were also skilled at identifying a man's peculiarities of penmanship) they got paid for expert testimony in court.

They would testify that no two machines—not even brand-new ones of the same make and model—are identical; that there were infinitesimal peculiarities in the molding of the type or in the alignment. And they would produce huge photographic blowups of single letters, place them side by side, and show even myopic jurors what they were talking about.

Most of the time they were quite right. One of the early cases in which the technique was used involved a number of government employees. A lot of forged orders had been issued from their particular department. Edward Hay, a Washington, D.C., handwriting expert, was called in. Using the same magnification techniques that he ordinarily employed to study the loops, dots and curlicues of handwriting, Hay tracked down the guilty typewriters and, soon afterwards, the culprits themselves.

Most typewriters have some obvious flaws; a broken letter, perhaps, or a character that is worn in some peculiar fashion. Its alignment may be unmistakably individual, especially if the machine has been used for a long time. And typists have revealing habits, perhaps something as simple as a funny way of misspelling some common word. On the other hand, if the machine in question is new, expert mechanics have spent considerable trouble trying to get rid of exactly the peculiarities that are the identification expert's stock in trade. And lots can happen to old typewriters between one day and the next. They can be realigned, for instance, which is part of a thorough overhaul. Or be given new type faces. For $20,000, or thereabouts, in fact, you can hire an expert repairman to duplicate any typewriter that ever wrote, as the Hiss defense did. The copy may not be exact. But it will be close enough to fool a good many experts. Of course fingerprints can be removed and faked, too, as every mystery-story fan knows. The fact that concealment and forgery are technically possible didn't stop the typewriter-identification experts any more than it has stopped fingerprinting. However, there was no point to the phony copy of the Hiss Woodstock, as the courts ruled, without some evidence that Whittaker Chambers hired one of the handful of typewriter men capable of making such a machine.

Luckily for typewriter detectives, most of their work is on an elementary plane. Crime by typewriter is usually a crude affair, like most counterfeiting. A good example turned up in the news not long ago, a swindle case in which somebody took about $180,000 from an international power-equipment company in Jaipur, India, and faked a receipt for the amount. There was no razzle-dazzle about it. The crook merely took a genuine document and added a couple of sentences on an entirely different machine.

Another variety of specialist was the typewriter collector. He got more fun than money out of it, although many persons who threw their old machines away in 1915, or sold them for junk, may regret it now. At the 1953 Antiques Fair in New York City a dealer was asking $40 for a decrepit Hammond of about 1910 vintage. There are hundreds of private typewriter collectors, led by Mr. Carl Deitz, of Milwaukee, who has at least 487 ancient machines in his possession, including a rare Crandall and an original model of the Cooper, which is unique.

Others regarded the typewriter as a medium for artistic expression. Some spent their time thinking up doodads that could be typed to decorate the page. They thought up an endless variety. A manual, *Ornamental Typing*, by George A. Flanagan, published by Gregg, contains a remarkable collection of ideas for jazzing up your correspondence in a way, to quote the author, "to catch the eye most effectively and to satisfy the esthetic taste."

If, for instance, you've written something of a tropical nature, you can type little rows of palm trees by writing capital "I"s and then, after resetting the line space, asterisks on top:

ᵼ ᵼ ᵼ ᵼ ᵼ ᵼ ᵼ ᵼ ᵼ ᵼ ᵼ ᵼ ᵼ ᵼ ᵼ ᵼ

And you can do neat little shields with "7" and capital "O":

ᗺ ᗺ ᗺ ᗺ ᗺ ᗺ ᗺ

The letters "f" and "j," struck one atop the other, make a nice

ᶨ ᶨ ᶨ ᶨ ᶨ ᶨ ᶨ , although it is hard to say exactly what

it is for. You can do

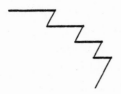

and then slash them with some impressive bolts of lightning:

or, with the underscore and the diagonal slash, create a beguiling ladderlike effect:

///

In addition to ornamentation, there were fine artists who made
typewritten pictures, portraits, say, of Theodore Roosevelt or
Woodrow Wilson. The idea is not completely dead, although the

subjects may have changed. Recent issues of the excellent magazine, *Today's Secretary*, which is partly printed in Gregg shorthand, to the dismay of any ignorant general reader, have featured typewritten art sent by subscribers. The big trend, as of now, is toward typewritten alphabetical samplers, in simulated cross-stitch. Montserrat Escardivol of Barcelona, who is a typist at $30 a month with the Barcelona police department, has developed fantastic skill at copying photographs, post cards, and reproductions of famous paintings on an old wide-carriage Underwood. She works on canvas, which enables her to type lots of letters close together or on top of each other without striking through, and she covers almost the entire surface with ink, delicately shaded, in seventeen different colors. She gets as much as $150 per picture. She has no intention of quitting the police department to spend her full time at art; it is far too much of a strain.

Finally, there were—and are—those who specialized in throwing old typewriting away: the file-systems experts and later the file-systems disposal experts.

The problem of gradual accumulation of typewritten correspondence, plus carbons, had worried typewriter users from the outset. Even before the invention of the writing machine, the crowding in file drawers had been abominable. The typewriter's advent made matters infinitely worse.

The first solution, logically enough, was more file drawers, more file clerks and better filing systems. By 1915 the science of what to file and how, and the business of supplying the furniture and equipment required, were keeping thousands of men busy.

But by the middle of the 1930's the growing accumulation of old typewriting began to overwhelm businessmen and business offices, and the files-disposal expert came into being.

For Some, Typing is One of the Fine Arts

He is a man, essentially, who knows how to throw typewriting away.

The files-disposal business boomed in about 1947 when the atom bomb threatened to clean out everybody's files with one whoosh, and businessmen thought that, if they didn't have such an awfully bulky lot of stuff to keep, they might save a few of the more important things in caves or underground vaults. In that year, with the help of $35,000 from the Rockefeller Foundation, a non-profit organization, the National Records Management Council, Inc., was formed to study the whole problem of cleaning out file drawers, and in the six years since then it has done a great job. The whole level of man's thinking on the subject has been raised. The knowledge the NRMC has acquired is available to everybody. Various profit-making companies that clean out files, like Shaw-Walker and Remington Rand, have learned a lot and have added ideas as well.

The general proposition is this: almost any business firm or government can do away with two-thirds of the papers it is saving.

Equitable Life started to clean out its files in 1938. It has thrown away only half of its old papers so far. But it had an awful lot to throw away: if, in '38, they had been arranged in one stack, the pile would have been fifty-one times as tall as the Empire State Building. Ten years ago Westinghouse started on a file-cleaning operation by destroying 120 railroad carloads of useless papers and transferring another three hundred carloads' worth to an archives building where nobody expects to read them. (They are held anxiously, just in case.) Mr. Emmett J. Leahy, the director of National Records Management Council, Inc., has been tidying up the Federal Government's files, an almost hopelessly complicated mess, occupying eighteen and a half million cubic feet of space. According to the magazine *Fortune,* Leahy's program is emptying file drawers at the rate of a million and a half a year. Which represents a paper-work saving, so far, of more than five million dollars.

There is little doubt that we as a nation are about to embark on an orgy of throwing out stuff, for the fifty-odd big outfits that have already tried the system Leahy and his colleagues preach, and have saved lots of money, are beaming with enthusiasm and telling their friends.

Remington-Rand has figured out that it costs from 80 cents to $1.30 to produce the average business letter. That's high enough without adding to the initial cost by keeping copies that nobody will ever read.

Carbons of correspondence fill about one file drawer out of every three, and the cost of maintaining one four-drawer file for a year comes to about $240, depending on the level of clerical salaries. That figure does not include the costs of supervision, building maintenance, taxes, or working space for the clerks around the space the file actually occupies.

And, according to NRMC, Inc., 95 per cent of all corporate paper work that has gotten more than a year old is never looked at again.

If, out of every hundred papers filed, twenty are referred to again, you've got a pretty good system, according to the experts in this new specialty. If as few as ten are consulted, you are probably filing more than you should. If it gets down to 1 per cent you're hoarding dead matter at live-file rates.

The disposal expert checks the files traffic. He sees who's putting what where, and who's looking at what from where. Then he applies his ratios, like the twenty out of one hundred rule. He checks the number of employees against the cubic feet of saved paper (hoping to find, in a general office of a manufacturing or sales company, not more than five cubic feet per person). Live files in the office itself should be just about as big, but no bigger, than the semi-dead files in the archives, a fancy word for cheap space in a storage warehouse in a less fashionable part of the city. Then, having made a diagnosis of what goes on, he advises the firm how to stop it.

Each company is a special case, and each department within the company must be considered separately. (Purchasing and Accounting, by and large, are the worst paper hoarders.) The cost of an expert's services therefore varies greatly. One good man's time is worth perhaps $150 a day, or $5,000 for six weeks' work. But his work can save a big company as much as $100,000 a year in released space, in cash returns on the sale of wastepaper, reclaimed file cabinets, and so forth.

Everybody has to hang on to *some* old stuff, of course. The federal, state and local laws demand it. If you're in the airlines business, for instance, you must hang onto your flight-movement records for six years because the Civil Aeronautics Board says so. But nearly all companies keep things longer than they have to. The throw-away specialists give businesses nerve enough to let the stuff go.

A big magazine, for example, may be persuaded to throw away the originals of its subscription orders after the necessary information has been transferred to stencils. Some risk is involved, to be sure. If the stencils are lost or destroyed and an irate subscriber claims he has twenty-three years to go on a twenty-five-year bargain offer, the magazine may have to take his word for it. But the chance is remote. The disposal expert shows that it costs more to keep those orders, in any case, than to fill any possible gyp claims. Or the expert may recommend that the executives, in answering letters, write in longhand down in the corner or on the reverse of the query. Or that they have things microfilmed, although, in some quarters, microfilming is in poor favor because it is regarded as squirrel-like and temporary; when the files of microfilm eventually crowd the president of the firm out of his office, then he is in really bad straits.

Procter & Gamble has a solution. It keeps its files down by preventing their growth, by edict. Each letter-dictating executive is allowed just one file drawer, or space enough for about thirty-five hundred sheets of paper. That and nothing more. He can file things galore until he fills up his drawer. But at that point he's done. He's either got to stop writing letters and keeping carbons, which is impractical. Or get busy and throw out some of the junk he's saved.

10 / Portables by Parachute

After the long period of concentration on typing speed, the typewriter industry began to emphasize quality and refinement. Speed was still important, to be sure, but after about 1930 the average buyer took it more or less for granted; he assumed, with justification, that all the best-known typewriters could write as fast as was necessary. Customers were no less demanding than they had been, but they were considerably less confused, for the industry had shaken down from more than a hundred competing firms to fewer than a dozen. The public had determined, by selection, the typewriter's general shape and approximate mechanical design. Inventors were working within those confines rather than trying to think up brand-new writing-machine concepts.

One occasionally bumps into an aged typist who says, nostalgically, that he thinks there hasn't been a decent typewriter on the market since the Blickensderfer or the Oliver, or who declares that since the Royal Number 10, or perhaps the Underwood Model 5, represented the pinnacle of achievement, the day "they" abandoned his favorite design was the day Disaster overtook and passed Education in their perpetual race. The old boy is off his rocker, although it may be simplest, on the whole, to agree with him that nothing is what it used to be, including the manners of the young, the beauty of women and the spring in his footstep. In point of fact, today's typewriter makes the semi-antiques look sick.

With only a handful of typewriters to consider and all of them front-strike, visible, type-bar-action machines, the buyer in the late 'twenties was free to focus on fine detail. Manufacturers could do no less. The hot competition, within a form now reasonably well defined, demanded—as it still demands—constant improvement.

In theory, inferior machines selling for low prices might have driven the first-class typewriters out of the market, or at least into a minor, de luxe corner of it. Several of the early firms were organized with not much more than low price as a principle; they planned to beat the leaders by underselling. There had been half a dozen machines designed to sell for $35 or less, and one, a pocket typewriter called the Virotyp, manufactured in France starting in 1914, which cost only $5. It was more toy than typewriter, but it was intended for grownups' use. Unhappily for those who had sunk money into the various cheap designs, the theory was entirely incorrect. The exact opposite happened: the good machines drove the bad out of circulation, a reversal of Gresham's monetary law. The typewriter in the United States was above all else a business tool. And businessmen, while they didn't want to pay a cent more than they had to, were vitally interested in quality. They considered real improvements or refinements as necessities rather than luxuries, and their secretaries were in complete agreement. Typists, on the whole, felt that the best was none too good. So that there was no significant demand in the United States for a stripped-down or second-class office machine, and consequently no one was able to pull off a *coup* comparable to Henry Ford's masterful stroke in the automobile field. (There was, however, a short-lived, tinny typewriter called the Ford, having no connection with the motor-car firm.) Businessmen, when it came to typewriters, wanted nothing less than the Cadillacs, Lincolns, and Chrysler Imperials.

In most lines of manufacture, the big seller is at least a notch or two down, in quality terms, from the high-fidelity, custom-built, connoisseur's model. Yet in typewriters the standard machine at the standard price is the best that money can buy, and, as a result, typewriter concerns have a tough time whenever they need a super-duper machine to present to visiting royalty or a record-smashing salesman; they never can think of anything to do to the regular stock model except to plate it with gold. At the St. Louis Fair in 1904, Harry Betts, who was in charge of the Oliver display, showed an $1,150 golden Oliver which, while it was not solid gold, glistened sufficiently to attract considerable attention. It had mother-of-pearl key-tops and a mother-of-pearl space-bar. Everything else, *except the working parts*, was 16 carat. The exceptions were the tip-off. Case-hardened steel is a better material than gold for type bars and carriage rails. And, as a matter of fact, mother-of-pearl keys, however jaunty, glare badly compared to dull green plastic.

The customer's attitude toward office typewriters carried over to portables. He not only wanted a portable to be de luxe in workmanship and writing ability, but he wanted it to resemble, as far as possible, the typewriters in his office.

One might have supposed that the $5 pocket Virotyp was a certain winner; it wrote, after a fashion, and for price and portability it was almost unbeatable. But buyers, in the main, did not take the adjective "portable" too literally. It might have been more accurate to call light typewriters "home" typewriters or "college dormitory" typewriters. The American market wanted a machine that could be moved easily from one room to another, which meant that it had to weigh about half as much as the office models. But the manufacturers were forbidden to leave off any of the major gadgets that the big typewriters had, and the portable's touch was to be as much like the standard's as possible, and it had to write just about as prettily. The Virotyp, in short, was far too portable to make any headway in the portable class.

It was a classic example of the desire to both eat and have one's cake. The big typewriters were no bigger and little heavier than was necessary, and they had no parts at all that had simply been tossed in for the fun of it. Typewriter manufacturers, faced with portable buyers' specifications, showed infinite patience, for they did not tell the customers to go jump in the lake. On the contrary, they started right out to attempt the impossible: to make a small, light typewriter that would print almost as well as the big, heavy ones. The best of today's portables, weighing considerably less than half as much as their big brothers, are a remarkable compromise between maximum printing ability and minimum weight.

It was not entirely reasonable, to be sure, that Americans should have been so interested in typewriter quality. It was merely a fact.

By the late 1930's typewriter men had two crystal-clear historical examples of the general proposition that merit tells. The Union Typewriter Company—and Remington, in particular, among its component firms—had made a bad error in hanging back on front-strike visibility. The proof was obvious. By 1910, or even earlier, Underwood was making and selling more type-

A 24 Carat Gold Typewriter

writers than any other company. Considering Remington's enormous head start, it was preposterous that an upstart should have found room inside along the rail to take over the lead. If Remington had started to make a visible in 1896 or even 1906, this might never have happened. But Remington was blind to the faults of the blind typewriter until 1910, and when it finally shifted over to the improved design, in that year, it was too late.

Underwood went on to dominate the field almost as completely as Smith's racing stable dominated the speed-contest world. Their peak was about 1920. All typewriter companies have always treated their exact unit sales figures as top secrets, but even Underwood's rivals admitted that the Model 5 sold in quantities equal to all the sales of all the other firms lumped together. Underwood representatives, in the years immediately after World War I, had a magnificent gimmick based on their company's extraordinary success, and the technique, in turn, had a good deal to do with keeping sales booming. If a prospect said anything about wanting to have a look, first, at another brand of typewriter, the Underwood man put on his most astonished face, as if such a notion were entirely lunatic. It would be a complete waste of time, he'd explain, sounding rather hurt because the customer had dared raise such an obnoxious idea.

"I'll tell you what I'll do," the Underwood salesman would say. "Just take your telephone book. Turn to any page. Pick any company in town. Give them a call and ask them what typewriter they're buying. And if they don't say "Underwood," I'll pack up and go away and never bother you again."

Few men could fail to be impressed by the sheer audacity of the dare, and practically nobody ever made the call for fear of sounding like a fool on the telephone; but even if the prospect checked the boast, Underwood had something like a fifty-fifty chance that he'd get the right answer.

Yet Underwood, despite the strength it gained while it basked in the sunlight of this delicious competitive situation, made a mistake. It was the same mistake Remington made a generation earlier: Underwood was so pleased with Model 5, and had done so spectacularly well with it, that the firm postponed the adoption of a new model. For the second time in typewriter history, the leader, seemingly in an impregnable position, left racing room for a rival; and left it voluntarily, so to speak; there was no rule that required the leader to cling to an outdated design.

Royal took the lead in about 1938 and holds it still, and while Royal can conceivably be overtaken, it isn't likely that the company will be the third to make the historic blunder. Royal won the lead with a new model. It changed its design immediately upon getting into first place, and again in 1949, and again in 1953. The men who run the company, headed by Fortune Peter Ryan and Allan A. Ryan, grandsons of Thomas Fortune Ryan, are determined that, if Royal is to be headed, a rival will have to push past. They do not intend to move away from the rail position, so far as quality and innovation are concerned, through lack of attention.

It is hardly necessary to add that the typewriter business is more complicated than a horse race. If there were nothing to it except design, the periodic meetings of salesmen and executives would be as quiet and calm as the lectures in the basement auditorium of the Museum of Modern Art. (They are nothing of the sort.) Salesmanship, sales organization, price, the personalities of individuals, luck and a thousand other factors enter into the story. A typewriter salesman with a proper attitude toward his occupation will insist that a typewriter company is no stronger than its sales staff, and he can support his argument with countless illustrations beginning with the fact that the Remington Model 4 got nowhere until Wyckoff, Seamans & Benedict stepped into the picture. Excellent designs, skillfully executed, have floundered and flopped for no good reason, as far as the eye can see, except that their salesmen were not quite up to the pace. There has never been a typewriter so superior, on intrinsic merit, that it has sold without human assistance. And so on and so forth.

Leave a handful of typewriter men alone together in a room, and the chances are that before long they'll start to torture each other with this question (or one of its infinite number of variations): "Which would you rather have; the best machine and the second-best sales force, or vice versa?" There is only one answer, which is to refuse the either-or choice and to demand the best of both.

Salesmanship had a lot to do with the big upsurge in the popularity of portables. There had been light machines, some of them called "folding" typewriters, from early in the game. Some customers had called for portability, according to Wyckoff's journal of reform, as soon as the first Remington appeared. Besides the Virotyp, there had been portable Blickensderfers, Hammonds, Coronas, Noiselesses, Allens, Bennetts, Americans and Remingtons, among a good many others. The 1906 Standard Folding Typewriter, forefather of the Corona, which was made in large part of aluminum, was one of the best of the early efforts. The Model 3, introduced in 1912, was called "Corona," and the pert little machine won a host of friends.

The key to portable selling was to establish the small machine as something quite separate from—though no less excellent than —an office typewriter. There was no sense in pretending that the half-sized machines could compete, letter for letter and carbon for carbon, with the big boys, but it was entirely sensible to push a light typewriter as a personal accessory. Hammond had tried to make the point. So had Corona. But the public had remained somewhat foggy on the distinction, if only because of the superabundance of makes and models in all sizes and weights, some designed for office work and others meant entirely for private letter writing. It was essential that the business typewriter be defined quite clearly before it was possible to make customers see that the portable was distinctly something else, a personality in its own right. The combinations and regroupings of the middle 'twenties helped sharpen the difference. The Rand Company bought both Remington and Noise-

First aid to KEEN AMBITION

A Portable Typewriter Ad of 1926

---

less. L. C. Smith and Corona combined. Elliott-Fisher bought Underwood. Those three, with Royal, were virtually the whole show. The big four's office typewriters, while quite different from each other, were all of one class, one weight, and one size (big). Any typewriter customer, however dense, could see that they were not portables.

Remington had been making a portable since 1920. Smith-Corona continued to make a portable. Underwood-Elliott-Fisher had a portable. Royal had no portable, but it did have George Ed Smith for its president. Smith was a salesman of the flamboyant school, a man who believed with all his heart in the value of publicity and promotion. In 1926, when Royal began to make a portable, Smith figured that it was important to introduce the junior machine with as loud a roll of drums as he could muster.

The first of Smith's tricks was color. Like all three of his competitors, he had his eye on the nation's fifteen million homes as the focus for his little Royals. He realized that the major-domo in each dwelling was a female, just as Hess had understood in 1904 that the secretary, rather than the boss, actually decided which office typewriter should be bought. Smith, thinking of the ladies, had the new portable painted in two tones in a full line of colors, from quiet buff-and-brown to brilliant green-and-blue, a total of more than five hundred combinations, including black-on-black for the ultra-conservative housewife, or the woman who did a great deal of formal entertaining.

His second trick was to buy the latest model Ford tri-motor airplane for $75,000, on the grounds—which Smith implied rather than stated openly—that there was no other means of transportation fast enough to get Royal portables to the hungry public. Royal had set up a new network of twenty-one hundred dealers who were to handle portables only. Their organization was almost completely separate from the force of six hundred salesmen working out of seventy branch offices who sold office standards. Portable outlets were, for the most part, home-appliance stores. The idea was that a housewife, looking for a waffle iron, might easily come home from the shop with a Royal portable instead, having been won over by the way its lovely colors matched her library drapes. Royal's airplane was not only going

Smith's $75,000 Airplane Had a Speed of 110 Miles an Hour

to fly portables from factory to dealer, but it was going to drop the machines by parachute, saving all the time that might have been lost in landing and unloading.

The stunt had everything. It had the biggest commercial airplane in the world, which was guaranteed to draw crowds of people whether they had any interest in typewriters or not. The new notion of dropping parachute-borne cargo was an eye-opener in itself. More important, from Smith's point of view, was the fact that the nation could hardly ignore the Royal portable as long as there was danger of being hit on the head with it. He wanted the ladies, in particular, to notice. But he wanted their husbands to understand, at the same time, that the machine was rugged despite its bright coat of enamel. A drop of several hundred feet from an airplane certainly suggested that the Royal was more than sturdy enough to withstand the normal shocks and bumps of ordinary home use.

The first show, starting a nation-wide tour that saw more than eleven thousand typewriters come plunging down to earth, was staged in Hartford despite a certain illogicality in flying Royals into the city where they were made. As a target, a big white sheet was spread out on the ground in the park near the State Capitol. Most of the leading citizens were present, led by Connecticut's Governor Trumbull. Charles B. Cook, head of the Royal factory and host for the occasion, later confessed that he wouldn't have dared to ask Trumbull to come if the Governor hadn't been a wild aviation enthusiast. Cook had another reason for feeling somewhat anxious about the affair. Having shepherded the portable through its factory production, he knew that throwing it out of an airplane, parachute or no parachute, was no way to treat his baby. He was particularly fearful that the wind might set the portables in their cardboard cartons swinging in the parachute shrouds, and if the boxes smacked down on their corners instead of their flat sides, there was a good chance the typewriters would be knocked completely out of kilter.

Luckily, Cook's fears were unjustified. The typewriters all landed beautifully. When the cartons were opened, they tested perfectly. The whole demonstration, in fact, was a huge success, and the space the newspapers gave it, not only in Hartford, but all over New England, far exceeded Smith's most optimistic estimates. In the entire eleven thousand drops, as a matter of fact, not more than half a dozen portables landed on their corners. The Royal ground crews, later on, were trained to watch

The Country Was Amazed to see Typewriters Falling from the Sky

carefully for the danger sign. Any machine that hit the ground incorrectly was put aside, if possible, and the cases opened were those that had fallen flat. The stratagem failed only once. As bad luck would have it, the failure occurred during a special demonstration for the benefit of Thomas Fortune Ryan. Smith arranged to drop a portable onto the lawn of the founding capitalist's estate in Virginia, just to prove to him what a wonderful stunt it was. (Ryan already had a Royal portable that had been delivered in a more prosaic manner.) That was the time, of all times, that the ground crew opened up a carton that had landed on its corner. Damned machine wouldn't write a letter.

Smith's genius at promotion was a big help to Royal, although he often worried the other executives who couldn't help feeling that working under his leadership had some of the less desirable aspects of dwelling on the slope of a volcano. He had a way of making his splashes sound more dangerous than they really were. For instance, he boasted that he'd paid seventy-five grand for his airplane without bothering to mention that, after he had reaped hundreds of thousands of dollars' worth of free advertising space, he planned to sell it at second-hand for half its initial cost. He decided to spend a fortune sponsoring the radio broadcast of the Dempsey-Tunney heavyweight championship fight, in September, 1926, but he didn't stop to explain that, because the coast-to-coast hookup would make radio history and the front page of every newspaper in the country would mention Royal, the stunt would be worth ten times its cost measured in column inches alone, not counting the good will among radio listeners, like the entire staff of the Easton, Pennsylvania, post office, who, among thousands of others, wrote Royal to thank the company for its public spirit. Smith's mind worked fast. He thought of publicity angles so quickly that he seldom had time to explain exactly what he had cooking. Per-

haps the best example of his facility was Smith's response when
he heard that the newspaper reporters, in one city after another,
had been stealing the portables during the post-inspection confusion. Smith thought for not more than a second or two before
he issued his order: "Don't do anything about it." The parachute
stunt got reams of free newspaper space. There might have been
much less if so many reporters had not written so fluently out
of a certain guilty sense of obligation.

The stock market crash in 1929 and the subsequent depression stopped the typewriter industry, much as it stopped industry as a whole. Some typewriter business experts, looking back,
judge that sales in 1930, '31, and '32 were not quite as bad as
they seemed to the typewriter companies at the time; the machine had become so essential to the American businessman
that he couldn't even cancel his orders or file a petition in bank-
ruptcy without having the papers typed. It had acquired something of the status of the potato among vegetables; no matter
how awful things got, man couldn't do without it. Sales were
poor, however. Man could go on using his old typewriter for
another year or two if he had to, or buy a rebuilt, second-hand
machine instead of a new one; and he was doing both. Gloom
pervaded the industry.

In 1933, International Business Machines entered the typewriter field by taking over a firm called Electromatic Typewriters, Inc., previously a part of the Northeast Electric
Company, which had been struggling for a decade to add elec-
tricity to the office standard machine. Northeast, in turn, had
taken its pilot models over from an inventor, James Smathers of
Kansas City, who had been working on them since 1914.

The idea of electric typewriting was older than the Remington Model 1. The Blickensderfer Electric of 1908 had been quite
an impressive affair. The Electric Power Typewriter Company

of Canada had marketed a sound, well-designed electric in 1906, and in 1910 Ellis had brought out a remarkable machine, electrically powered, which was not only a typewriter but an adding machine and a billing machine to boot. All these noble experiments had ended in disaster.

A consensus of typewriter industry opinion in 1933 would have held, surely, that IBM had failed to Think. Not only was the typewriter business bad in general, but electrics, in particular, had repeatedly proven a dismal flop. By 1954, of course, all the major typewriter producers, with the exception of Smith-Corona, were making and selling electrics.

That is not quite the same as saying that IBM's 1933 move was perfectly timed, for even now, after twenty-one years, total electric sales are hardly worth mentioning compared to total standard and portable sales. Nevertheless, IBM deserves full credit for having rescued an idea from desuetude. It seems more than likely that electric typewriters, in the future, will occupy a far larger place in the typewriter scheme of things than they do right now. (Of all the typewriters in use today, roughly 5 per cent are electrics.) If typewriter history teaches anything, the importance of electrics will be decided by secretaries and typists. And second, although the boss may shake his head with dismay at the fact that an electric costs at least $100 more than a non-electric, the price differential won't be an important matter.

The typist has not yet brought in her final verdict. Some girls, having tried powered typing, are devoted converts who will never go back to the non-electric way if they can avoid it. Others feel, with equal intensity, that finger power is best.

Perhaps the biggest block in the way of electrics is inertia of just the kind that has prevented keyboard reform. An expert touch typist, on her first day or two with an electric, is almost certain to have a wretched time. She has to unlearn something—although not much—of what she knows. The position of the keys may be exactly the same as on her non-electric, but there are a few new controls in unusual positions. And, since the keys go down of their own accord after they have been depressed a prescribed distance, the monster feels as if it had a certain will of its own; her first few hundred words, at least, are bound to be peppered with extra letters and unnecessary spaces that seem to have written themselves without anyone's by-your-leave. The expert, unless she is prepared for a brief period of typing humiliation, may give the electric up before she has started to get the hang of it. (Careful experimentation has shown, on the other hand, that a complete tyro can learn faster on an electric than on a non-electric; its power compensates for the weakness of his third and little fingers. He achieves, electrically, the strength his mother had to learn by hours of tedious practice.)

Furthermore—to continue the negative side of the case—electrics hum. The hum is faint, and it gets fainter year by year as electrics are constantly improved. Yet it is a hum, and, to a few sensitive souls, the thought of one's typewriter sitting smugly, humming during the intervals, is obnoxious. (It hums all the time the switch is in the On position, but the sound can only be heard when the typing stops.) There are one or two other drawbacks of a practical, non-psychological nature. Naturally, since the motor is an extra, electrics require a little more servicing, and the cost of maintenance is a little higher. When something goes wrong, the secretary hardly dares plunge into the machine's insides with her bobby-pin to repair the fault—though, from management's point of view, this should doubtless be counted as a blessing.

But there are real advantages. Enough of them so that many typewriter men regard the future growth of the electric segment of the business as a sure thing. The printing itself looks lovely, because the type bar hits hard and every stroke has the same force as its neighbors regardless of the pressure on the key— the idea that fascinated James Hammond in 1880. An electric will make more and better carbons than a non-electric. It saves an appreciable amount of the typist's physical energy, largely because the carriage return, the back-space, and the shift—the heaviest motions in typing—are electrified, of course, along with the keys. Once she has mastered the beast, a girl can turn out her normal day's quota of letters and memoranda and feel, by 5:30, that she's done less than a non-electric day's work. Some motion studies have been made which indicate that the energy-saving factor may be as much as 6 per cent. Which is pure bonus as long as the boss doesn't expect his patient stenographer to accomplish 20 per cent more, now that he's broken down and bought her an electric.

As far as the difficulty of switching from non-electric to electric is concerned, that barrier may be hurdled by a frank-and-honest approach. Star typists don't seem to mind having a rough time with the new gadget provided it's well understood, by all hands, that a rough time is what they're *supposed* to have. One Cincinnati firm, in particular, seems to have by-passed all tears and temper tantrums by a simple gambit. When it introduces a stenographer to her new electric, the office manager says, "Take the next couple of days off. Don't do any work at all. Just come in on your regular schedule and play with this thing. Why don't you write a letter to your brother at Fort Dix?" At the end of two days, the company has found, almost any typist will have licked her transition blues and be ready to go.

One pro-electric factor, however, may well outweigh all the rest. IBM's big pitch for its electric has been aimed at the tycoon. The stress has been on the argument, subtly couched, that any

businessman, by going electric, can show he's a big operator—
or, at the very least, that he has paid that extra something for
his writing machine. But it is interesting to note that, in pro-
moting their electrics, Royal, Remington and Underwood (with
a collective 190 years of experience in the game) are aiming,
with at least an equal concentration of fire, at the tycoon's
typist. An electric on her desk, of course, proves to the office
that she's not only liked, but well liked. For, *quod erat demon-
strandum,* the business department has had to come through
and get her the premium-priced writing machine. This factor
could be the straw that will tip the balance in the electric's
favor. For if, by 1964, most business letters are written by
electrically powered typewriters, it will be because that all-
powerful girl has decided they should be.

11 / Adjuster at Work

It's too bad that one of those pioneer writing-machine experimenters—Judge Burt, for instance—can't meet Horace Stapenell of 1803 Broad Street, Hartford, Connecticut. (And quite impossible, because Burt and Stapenell are a century apart in time.) Stapenell is a typewriter man, although not a typewriter inventor. He is one of the best of the most highly skilled workmen in the factory of the Royal Typewriter Company, which makes more typewriters than any other firm in the world. Burt would be wildly excited, with typical enthusiasm, if he could watch Stapenell at work, for the jump from tool shed to modern factory, all fantasy aside, is close to unbelievable.

What Stapenell does, specifically, is called "final adjusting," or "C–40," if you are one Royal employee explaining what job you're on to another Royal employee. Final adjusting, as the name suggests, is the last step in typewriter manufacture before packing and shipping. Stapenell works exclusively on standard-model machines in a department, 10–C, in one wing of the long, four-story plant, and he's one of a couple of hundred men all doing the same thing. Portables and electrics get their final adjustments in other departments in other parts of the factory and, as an indication of the size of the establishment, although Stapenell knows the location of those other departments, and has friends working in both, he almost never wanders that far away from his own job. 10–C men hang around together, sit at the same tables in the mammoth cafeteria, and talk largely about 10–C affairs. If a workman leaves 10–C and goes to another department, he inevitably loses touch with his old pals, like a city dweller forced into the suburbs on account of the new baby.

Stapenell is fifty-three years old, tall, and as thin as a rail. He wears glasses with thick reddish frames in a style that approximates the owlish vogue among Madison Avenue advertising executives, a confusing note, for otherwise his work clothes and his manner suggest a professional out-of-doors man of some sort. His sleeves are rolled to the elbows, and his forearms are marked with blurred tattooing. He wears a denim work apron over his shirt and trousers. If he were not a typewriter man, Stapenell might be a fishing guide, for fishing is his great leisure-time passion. He speaks softly and in a pattern that follows the New England stereotype almost to perfection: economy of phrase, a nasal twang, and a broad "a" on words like "park" and "car." Like so many stereotypes, this one is overthrown by the facts; Stapenell's accent is really English. He was born and lived in England until he was fourteen. He came to the United States with his mother and a brother shortly before World War I, and when he was eighteen he served a hitch in the coast artillery. During World War II he was drafted, for a brief spell, before the army realized that he'd be more valuable as a high-ranking war worker than as a private soldier. Except for those two military interludes, typewriters have been the focus of his whole

One Corner of Department 10-C, Final Adjustment

working life. On January 29, 1954, he celebrated his thirtieth year as a Royal factory employee.

There's no better final adjuster in the business. Stapenell's rating, technically, is matched by a good many other 10–C men, but technical ratings don't tell everything. When the five millionth Royal standard moved through his department, not long ago, Stapenell was the man picked to do the work on it. A long tag accompanies each typewriter, as it gradually takes shape, from one department to the next, and every man or woman who works on the machine's assembly signs his personal number on the tag to show that he has completed and takes responsibility for his particular task. Stapenell's personal number is 92. When 92 appears on a tag in the space after operation C–40, it is taken for granted by everyone that the machine's adjustment conforms, in all respects, to the exacting set of specifications. It is a finished typewriter. An inspector may possibly give it one more look, for spot checks are continuous and are made without consideration for the numbers on the tags. If, however, an inspector found a serious flaw in the final adjustment of a typewriter marked 92, that would be big news. The 10–C men in the cafeteria would talk about it all through lunch.

Stapenell spends as long as three hours adjusting a single typewriter. If he (or any other final adjuster) completes four machines a day, the foreman of 10–C, Joseph Grazulwich, is pleased. To anyone who thinks of factories in automaton terms, with each worker adding one bolt or tightening one screw as the product glides past, this may come as a surprise. A two-hour average may seem long, especially in view of the fact that before a final adjuster takes over the typewriter is complete except for a few fittings and the outside dust-protection covers. It not only writes, but another highly skilled workman, an aligner, in another department, has written on it for as long as an hour, making sure that the letters and characters all print neatly and clearly in impeccably straight lines. Typewriter manufacture is not a belt-line proposition. It is primarily bench assembly—slow, painstaking, and done by hand.

One Thursday afternoon, several months ago, Stapenell performed the final adjustments on HH 5166247, a standard-width carriage machine with a standard keyboard. When he came back to Department 10–C from lunching in the cafeteria, HH 5166247 was waiting not far from his workbench on a dolly something like a rolling bookcase along with fifteen or twenty other typewriters ticketed for other adjusters. In theory, neither Stapenell nor any one of the other workmen in the plant has to wait idly for material to work on, and the theory corresponds reasonably closely to the fact, not by accident, but because a small army of logistics experts in Production Control (D–24) spends its full time struggling to maintain order, watching the flow of materials, parts and partly finished typewriters with infinite suspicion, ready to hurry up Plating, if Plating is sluggish, or to slow down Carriage Assembly if Carriage Assembly gets going too fast, or to explain, as politely as possible, that unless Screw Manufacturing gets on the ball and turns out more screws, the end of the world is not far distant. Production Control's function would be comparatively simple if the factory were, say, twice its size, for then there'd be room to keep big reserve piles of everything all over the plant, and squirrels could be put in charge to take the place of the efficiency engineers. In the meantime, however, it's up to D–24 to make sure that 10–C always has just enough typewriters on hand, but never too many.

Stapenell picked up HH 5166247 off the dolly, along with a paper package containing parts and a ribbon, and carried them to his bench, next to one of the windows. The department is on the factory's third floor, and the long narrow room, with three exposures, has excellent natural light, augmented by batteries of fluorescents. A spot by the window, none the less, is one of the minor privileges that go with thirty years' seniority. The final adjusters work on small wooden desks arranged in rows with a wide aisle down the center, as if they were in an enormous schoolroom. The desks are as low as typewriter tables, but they have a contraption in the center of their top surfaces, a rotating frame rather like a lazy Susan. The typewriter, minus side, back and top covers, fits into a shallow brass form, and the form fits into the frame. It's hinged so that, once the machine is locked into place, the adjuster can lift the keyboard up, turning the typewriter onto its back, and work at its insides from underneath. He can also spin the machine around, with a finger touch, so that it faces him any way he likes. Stapenell's wooden chair, like all the other adjusters' chairs, is low. The typewriter, on this frame, sits high. The printing point of HH 5166247, once Stapenell had fastened it onto the lazy Susan, was on a level with his eyes. He had to reach up quite a way to touch the keys.

Altogether, final adjusting involves about twenty separate functions. Each part of the process is defined with meticulous care, and the results one adjuster gets are exactly like another's. Within some limits, however, a man can take the twenty parts in whatever order he prefers. Stapenell has a routine of his own, developed over the twenty-eight years he has been on final adjusting. (He started at Royal, after he had been to the company's training school, as a preliminary adjuster.) He follows his own sequence, typewriter after typewriter, without any variation, so that he never has to worry about having forgotten one of the steps; it would be impossible for his hands to skip a step even if his thoughts wandered off to the fish in the Black Ledge, his favorite among local trout streams. To anyone except another final adjuster, furthermore, Stapenell's method is so much like everyone else's method that he'd hardly mention the differences or understand the advantages. They are important to Stapenell, however. They are the distinctions between working at a craft and working as a machine.

As he got to work he opened up the paper package and spread out its treasures—tiny screws and odd-shaped black metal fittings, a bell, a couple of scales, and the buff-colored covers—on the right-hand side of his desk. Then he removed the tag, which had been tied to the carriage with half a dozen other papers, and read one of them, an order sheet, with particular care. Stapenell looked to see that HH 5166247 had, as it was supposed to have, a normal-width carriage (and not any one of the half dozen more-than-normal widths), élite type (not pica or any one of the infinite variety of special-order faces and sizes) and a standard keyboard (without any extra or unusual signs or characters, and without any change in the ordinary arrangement of the keys). He was just checking. If there'd been any error, HH 5166247 would have gone right back to the department that had made the mistake. HH 5166247 was okay. Stapenell tucked the papers away, for the time being, in his desk's one small drawer.

His second concern was the ring-and-cylinder adjustment. The ring is part of the segment, the slotted, curved, chunk of metal that holds the type bars. The cylinder is the main rubber roller, often called the platen. Their position—especially their relationship, one to the other—is a big factor in determining how prettily the typewriter types. One can see the ring easily enough, by lifting the top cover and peering down. It's the crescent-shaped ridge of metal, made out of steel, a couple of inches below the printing point and just above the slots in the segment. It protrudes about an eighth of an inch forming the first ledge where eraser crumbs may accumulate. If you move one type bar, very slowly, until the type touches the paper, you may be able to see that the typewriter's shank hits that ring just as the type strikes the ribbon and the paper against the cylinder. The tough ring, not the rubbery cylinder, stops the type bar. Pound away at the keys as hard as you dare, the ring prevents the type

---

Automatic Slotting Machine Cutting Two Segments at the Same Time

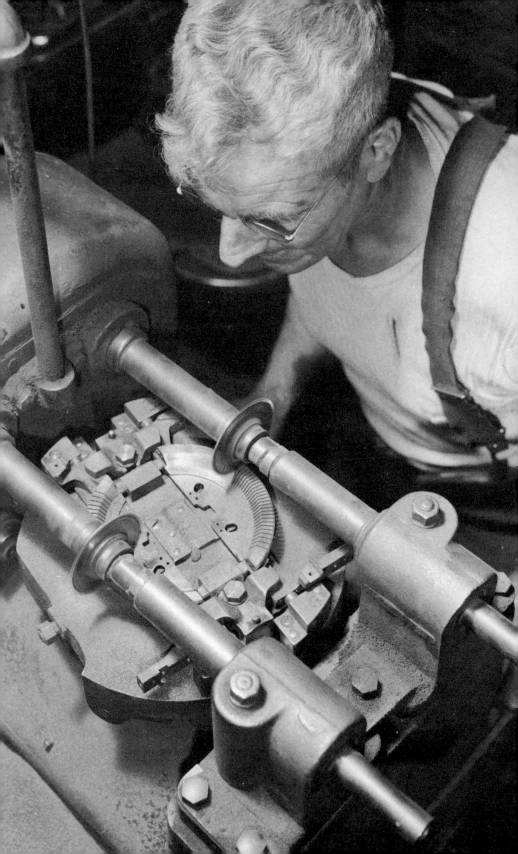

from crashing into the rollers. All you achieve is a slightly darker impression. If the ring protrudes too far, however, and stops the type bar short of the roller, there's no impression at all, and consequently no writing. Or if the ring is set too deeply into the segment, and the type bars travel too far, you get unpleasantly dark, blurred printing and holes in the paper instead of periods—a characteristic of some tired old machines whose worn rings have had more pounding than they can bear. Neither of these drastic extremes worried Stapenell. He was interested in making sure that HH 5166247's action was perfect, neither a shade too hard nor a shade too light. He took a thin strip of typewriter paper, and held it against the roller at the printing point. Then, moving the type bar very slowly, he tried one letter. When the key was all the way down, the face of the type held the strip in a delicate grip against the roller. Stapenell gave a little tug. It still held. He tugged a little harder and it came free. His fingers could tell, by experience, whether the type's hold on the single thickness of paper was tight enough without being too tight. He made the test with several keys on both ends of the cylinder as well as in the middle. He found that the right-hand end of the cylinder was a trifle too far forward; the hold on the paper gauge was ever so slightly on the heavy side. He unscrewed a couple of screws, moved the roller an imperceptible distance, and then repeated the paper-strip test to make certain that, in fixing the right-hand roller adjustment, he hadn't knocked either the left-hand end or the center out of line. In five minutes or so the first adjustment was finished. The time was fast, partly because Stapenell hadn't had to move the ring, which is adjustable, but only the cylinder. The task might have taken two or three times as long if the assemblers, the preliminary adjusters, and the adjusters who had worked on HH 5166247 before it got to Stapenell had left him more to do.

Stapenell already had an idea that the type was hitting the roller at the proper height, which was his next concern. The cast type is not flat, as it appears to a casual observer, but curved; a shallow concave that matches the convex roller surface so that the top of each letter prints as firmly as the bottom. The fit is precise, provided that the type strikes exactly according to design, and each letter curves snugly into place. Should the strike be a little high or a little low, however, printing quality would suffer. The matching curves, instead of nesting together, would clash. The result: dark tops and light bottoms, or light tops and dark bottoms, or, in a really critical case, ghost letters showing faintly between the lines. Stapenell could tell, from the paper-hold test, that the fit was good. He also could judge the height of the strike by eye, and feel that the shift was working properly. Throughout final adjustment Stapenell has a general sense of the machine as a whole, even while he is concentrating on a specific part. All his senses except taste are involved. He doesn't often smell anything wrong, despite the theory that nothing else can account for his ability to tell, from some distance, that one miserable little screw probably needs another millimeter's turning. He may not make a correction immediately, because he takes one step at a time in an orderly fashion, but he usually spots trouble, if there is any trouble, within the first few minutes of the long procedure.

Stapenell ran a sheet of paper into HH 5166247, despite his feeling that the shift was all right, and wrote a series of capital and lower case "n"s, like this: nNnNnNnNnNnNn. They made a perfectly straight line along the bottom, proof that the distance the segment shifted was correct. He examined the tops of the letters, comparing them, for darkness, with the middles and bottoms. They were as even as could be, proof that the curve of the type fitted the curve of the cylinder to perfection.

Then Stapenell checked the paper feed.

Putting a sheet of paper in a typewriter is easy enough. Some typists, lulled into complacence by the operation's simplicity, fail to realize that there are three rollers in all, two of them invisible beneath the main roller. The feed rolls, like almost everything else about a typewriter, are complicated. A good paper-feed system takes hold of anything from one thin sheet of onion-skin paper to a thick bundle of regular paper, carbons, and copy sheets, and holds it in a firm grip that is, at the same time, so light that the black doesn't come off and smear the duplicates. It guides the paper underneath the main roller, past the two feed rolls, and up into daylight again without messing up any corners or edges, and perfectly straight, without a suspicion of wrinkling or crinkling, and with the pages firm and flat. There is no slipping; ten lines after a mistake, the operator can turn

Each of the Type Bars Is Bent to its Own Particular Shape

back and hit the space on the nose. She can jab at the error with her eraser, and still the paper maintains position. She can even rip a sheet of airmail stationery out of the machine by pulling at it, in defiance of her secretarial-school faculty, and the amiable paper feed lets go so easily that the tissue doesn't tear. What a good paper-feed system achieves, in short, approaches the impossible.

Part of the secret is the position of the three rollers with relation to each other. Part is their relative diameters, and their resiliencies. The shape of the sleek, chromium-plated guide pan that steers the paper has a lot to do with it. But the most important trick about paper feed is the spring-mounting of the first feed roll and, on the Royal, of the front roll as well, an exclusive feature of which the company is very proud. The springs provide the gentle, vital tension. They give the paper feed its extraordinary knack of holding firmly, moving easily, and letting go promptly, whether the load is thick or thin. Stapenell lifted the main roller out of position. He examined the paper guide pan carefully, looking for flaws or scratches. He ran his finger tips over it lightly to see whether it felt as smooth as it looked. He poked at the two feed rolls, like a doctor feeling for a broken bone, judging the strength of the resistance they offered, and checking whether they moved down and back into place with the proper ease and effortlessness. Then he replaced the main roller. Using the same sort of paper strips as in the ring-and-cylinder test, he tested on the right, on the left and in the center. Everything was in order.

Stapenell swung HH 5166247 around on the rotating frame until its open back faced him, and fixed a small part, the tabular stop release, into place. He moved the carriage back and forth, setting and clearing various stops, and watching closely to make sure that the action was positive and decisive. A tough test for a tabulator is to set stops at, say, a dozen spaces in a row; and then, using the tabular key as if it were the space bar, to make the carriage walk along from one space to the next. The carriage moves as the tab key is released, not on the down-stroke. But otherwise the action should be as certain and smooth as any well adjusted space bar's. HH 5166247's was.

Stapenell tried the automatic left- and right-hand margin mechanism, making sure that their actions were as magic as the Royal trademark declares. He tested the margin-release key, peering down the carriage from the right end, and then spinning the machine around and peering from the left end. When the margin-release key is pressed down, and the margin stop bumper pulls back out of the way, the carriage glides past, or should glide past, with complete freedom. The bumper doesn't get very far out of the way. The clearance is not nearly as wide as a dime's thickness, so that there's no room for *approximate* adjustment. Unless everything is exactly where it should be, a margin release works erratically, which is the worst sin.

Stapenell tried the space bar, paying particular attention to its free play. A space bar goes down about a quarter of an inch before it trips the escapement and lets the carriage move on a notch; it should go down under very gentle pressure, yet not too gentle. Most of the time, the typist's thumbs hit the space bar somewhere near the center. But not always. Sometimes the pressure lands way out on either end, perhaps not with a thumb at all, but any old finger. However and wherever the space bar is struck, it's expected to work. Always. It's expected to move fast. It's expected to move the carriage one space, and only one. The spacer is used more often than any other key on the machine— if one may call a bar a key—and it must never fail. As one veteran typewriter man once said, "A typewriter company's entire reputation is at stake every time a typist hits at the space bar."

Meaning that an otherwise first-class machine, cursed with a space bar that lags or stutters, is promptly and irrevocably damned as a pile of junk, and the name of the manufacturer, henceforth, is Mud. Stapenell tested the space bar on HH 5166247 with considerable sobriety, not because he was thinking about Royal's reputation, but because his sensitive touch detected a trace of stiffness in its action. He tapped both its ends. He set the margins as wide apart as they would go, and tried spacing on the carriage's extremes (almost any space bar performs reasonably well in center field). The action was admirably precise. And yet, in the free play, before the tripping of the escapement, Stapenell felt some friction. It was nothing that anyone except a final adjuster would notice. Perhaps another adjuster would not have agreed that there was a fault. To be on the safe side, Stapenell tipped HH 5166247 over on its back in the hinged frame, exposing its underside. He opened the drawer of his desk and took out a small bottle of machine oil. He picked up an artist's brush of an extremely small size, dipped it in the oil, wiped it against the neck of the bottle, and brushed one of the surfaces of the long space-bar support arms with two or three short, delicate strokes. He tried the free play again. Okay.

So far—except for assembling the tab stop release—Stapenell had worked mainly as an inspector. He had been prepared to adjust anything he found that needed adjustment, but he had mostly just checked. He hadn't expected to find much wrong, and, on the whole, HH 5166247 had passed its tests with honors. Sometimes one small part is only a mite out of line and yet it holds Stapenell up for a long time before he sets it right, for one adjustment may involve several others; and then, when he is done with the several, he may have to go back to the first and reset it all over again, and then the several, and so forth. There may be a number of such patience-testing ordeals during one final adjustment, which is why Stapenell cannot follow a rigid timetable. The minutes lost on a hard adjustment, he hopes, will be gained on an easy one. In due time the average works out to a little more than two hours.

"People don't understand about typewriters," Stapenell once said. "I often explain about my job; how sometimes one machine goes through like a shot, and other times I fiddle around all afternoon before I'm finished. Some people jump to the conclusion that the difficult machine is a lemon. Not true. You have to understand that typewriters are like watches. They need regulating. You take making a fine watch. It may keep perfect time, right off the bat, before the factory regulators have done anything to it. Or, on the other hand, it may require lots of adjusting. But finally, when it's adjusted right, one watch is like the others; they all keep perfect time, and 'good' or 'bad' doesn't figure into it. That's just the way it is with typewriters."

Stapenell's next job was another assembly. (There is no shortage of assemblers among the sixty-five hundred factory employees; final adjusters double as assemblers simply because the last few parts, in their places, would block the way to various set screws, lock nuts, bearing surfaces and other key adjustment points.) He had to put together and attach the small bell that tings to warn of the right-hand margin's approach. His fingers are long, and his hands do not appear especially dextrous. Their movements are rather slow. But it is a long time between Stapenell's fumbles. The tiny parts of the bell and its miniature hammer behaved as if they had realized, in advance, that they had met their master. A screw about the size of a cigarette lighter's flint fits through a hole in the center of the bell into a matching hole drilled in the metal plate at the back of the typewriter. The screw is too small to pick up conveniently; a man could go out of his mind merely trying to get hold of it, let alone put it in

Winding Springs for the Magic Margin Mechanism

its place. Stapenell picked up the smallest of his several screw-drivers. He pressed down on the snippet of metal with the tip of his forefinger, and lifted it off the surface of his desk. While the screw was still sticking to his finger, he mounted it on the tip of his screwdriver, where it was held, magically, by the tiny indentation in its head. Then, with his other hand, he picked up the bell and held it in place, with the two pin-sized holes match-ing. With the screw riding precariously on the tip of the screw-driver, and with his hand as steady as a rock, Stapenell plunked the screw's business end right into place on the first stab. With one turn of his wrist, the tiny threads were engaged. Two more turns and the bell was firmly fastened in place. The bell-mounting part of the assembly had taken not more than five seconds. In about that much more time he attached the midget clapper. Then Stapenell put the tiny spring in its place, with a calm, unflustered air that would have driven all Christmas-morning amateur mechanics insane with jealousy. He hung one end of the spring on its little mounting. Then, still using the smallest screwdriver, he hooked onto the other end of the spring, stretching it slightly, swinging it around one gadget and poking an end through a needle-sized hole, and bent the end down with a wrist twist. That was all there was to that. Stapenell plinked the hammer against the bell a couple of times, listening to the tone. Then he spun the typewriter around, and tested the action of the bell several times, swinging the carriage back and forth and noting that the hammer release worked, as it should, every time the carriage got to within nine spaces of the right-hand margin stop.

Stapenell was once asked why he became a typewriter mechanic. "It was because I was too dumb to be an engineer," he replied. It was characteristic that he put his job, and his excellent record at that job, in such downbeat perspective. He is a modest man. He might have made a good engineer. In the opinion of his superiors, led by E. J. Cichowitz, chief assembly inspector and one of the most knowledgeable of typewriter men, Stapenell is an almost perfect employee as far as reliability and integrity are concerned. One of the reasons Stapenell did not become an engineer was that, when he got out of the coast artillery, the idea that Royal would give him a job and pay him while he learned the mysteries of adjusting at the factory school was a bargain he could hardly afford to resist. He stayed, once he'd started, because he liked the work. He earns good wages.

He owns a two-and-a-half-story house, white with green trimmings, where he lives in a bachelor apartment on the second
floor. He drives a light blue 1953 Dodge to work every day,
despite the plant's propaganda campaign against it. (The two
huge parking lots are crowded to capacity.) He gets a three
weeks' vacation in the middle of the summer, and usually takes
a trip to Maine or Canada for the fishing. On top of his generally satisfactory lot in life, he likes typewriters. "I get tired of
the routine," Stapenell says. "Whenever there's a new model,
or a change in a part, I get a kick out of it; and I like working
on the special-order jobs, too, just for the sake of change, even
though they may be some extra trouble. But I don't mind the
regular grind at all. I don't know. There's a lot of satisfaction
in it."

The engineers, as well as a good many social theorists of every
stripe, have been talking for years about the coming "second
industrial revolution" that will replace the Stapenells of society
with electronic machines, relieving men's boredom in the same
way that the first industrial revolution relieved his muscles.
There is little question, moreover, that IR II is on the way, for
in some industries, notably those where fluid handling is a
major chore, like oils and chemicals, it has already arrived.
Progress can't be stopped just because Stapenell, the potential
beneficiary of "automatism," doesn't want to be relieved from
his boring routine, and isn't even sure that he's more bored than
the next man. Luckily for Stapenell, the most marvelous of the
thinking apparatuses are not yet within striking distance of the
final adjusters' league. Many of the machines employed in typewriter manufacture are miraculous. They grow capable of more
and more of the work, especially in the departments that punch
out parts, thread screws, plate, finish castings, paint, temper
steel, wind springs and all that sort of thing. Machines can also

do a little assembly. The most talented, to date, is working on automobiles, not typewriters: it is a wonder apparatus that can take four or five parts, put them together into a radiator cap, and then look at the finished cap to see whether it passes inspection. In general, however, simple assembly is too hard for machinery, even machinery with a "brain" the size of a seven-room apartment that can complete more computations per second than a thousand mathematicians figuring away for a thousand years. But assembly is the least of Stapenell's job. The tricky part is using his three senses to compare the given typewriter with his vast accumulation of knowledge about what typewriters should be; and then selecting one course of corrective action out of thousands of possibilities. Stapenell makes such judgments several times per second, even when he's daydreaming about the Canadian trout. To date no machine can do anything of the kind, no matter how long it thinks, nor how hard it concentrates.

Stapenell's next step was to assemble the carriage-support rail—"the channel," in his own phraseology—which is installed after all other adjustments that affect carriage position and carriage travel are complete. The rail is a long metal track at the machine's top rear, bolted securely to the base. A fat little wheel, attached to the carriage, runs along the track between two flanges. The purpose is to lend the carriage support, and to help hold it in position, so that it will ride back and forth with the prescribed smoothness. Most of the carriage's weight rides on ball bearings on the main track, directly beneath the main roller. There's also a roller bearing, running along a second rail, straight back of the printing point, which is designed to absorb the pounding of the type bars. The third and rearmost track

Brazing Operation on Universal Bars

carries some weight and guards against emergencies like someone picking up the machine by the main roller knobs or knocking the typewriter off its stand onto the floor, which is a bad way to treat it. Stapenell fixed the channel in place on its sturdy brackets. He picked out a small, cylindrical weighing scale from among his tools. He pushed the carriage to the extreme left, and hooked one end of the scales onto the right-hand end of the carriage, and gave a slow, steady pull. The indicator moved up from zero to just a shade beyond the two-pound mark.

According to specifications, the tension on the carriage, with the tension control knob set exactly in the middle of its range, should measure exactly two pounds. But, as Stapenell once explained to an apprentice adjuster, a shade beyond two pounds, at this particular stage, is the target he aims for. "I don't know why it is," he said, "but if I put her exactly on two now, she'll run a little light by the time the whole job is finished. So you want to set the tension just a hair beyond two. It's something sort of mysterious." Stapenell left HH 5166247 just as she ran, a shade beyond two pounds.

The Royal has four separate ruled scales, marked off in letter spaces, to tell the typist just where she is, to check the straightness of the paper insert, to position margins, to set up tabular columns, to find the middle of the page, and so forth. They are co-ordinated; space number 20 on one scale corresponds to number 20 on the others. Four seems a lot, in the abstract, but each has a definite function of its own, and none has been added merely to fancy up the looks of the machine. For instance, on the question of getting a sheet of paper in straight: if the paper guide is in position at zero on the paper-guide scale, and if the paper is inserted competently, and if the paper feed works properly, the left-hand edge of the paper, when it appears from beneath the cylinder, will hit the zero mark on the main cylinder scale. Then, as it is turned up the next couple of inches, and the paper-lock bar is brought down to hold it in place, it will hit zero again on the paper-lock bar scale. There is no need, at that point, to question the fact that it is in straight. Any added check, like rolling the sheet halfway out of the typewriter to see whether the top edge squares with the bottom edge, is a complete waste of time.

Stapenell checked the calibration of the scales, and assembled and attached the card-and-writing-line scales, immediately to the right and left of the printing point, which fit onto the card-holders assembly. (The card-holders are the two saucy little ears that stick up to keep post cards or file cards against the roller.) A typist uses the card-and-writing-line scales to determine the exact position of a letter. The top of the scale and the bottom of the writing line coincide. Letters with the lowest descenders ("y," "p," "g," and "q") sit on it like cats on a fence. The vertical, unnumbered, marks on the scale hit the spaces in dead center, so that by lining up the "i"s, the "t"s, or the "l"s perfectly, a typist can add a letter to a line she's already finished without hitting to the right or left of the proper place. Stapenell fixed the scales' position by simply reversing that process. He wrote a series of "i"s and wiggled the scale back and forth until the markings matched the letters. Then he tightened down the screws and nuts that hold the scales in place.

He tested the ribbon reverse, both manual and automatic. He tested the ribbon-travel mechanism using the space bar alone; if the ribbon moves properly on the space bar's action, there's no question that it will work when the keys are hit. He examined the ribbon vibrator to see that it popped up and down effortlessly on its twin columns. He checked the back-spacer by hitting it and a letter key together, a coincidence that would never come up in actual typing unless by accident. According to specifications, the back-spacer's action must be strong enough to move the carriage back against the full forward impetus of the spring. He put on a new ribbon, all black, with ridiculous ease. He had both spools in place with the ribbon strung between them before he attempted to thread the cloth through the vibrator; there was no chance that a twist in the fabric could sneak in. To obtain maximum finger space, Stapenell locked down the shift key and pushed the letters "g," "b" and "h" at the same time, so that they locked, raising and holding the vibrator at the top of its travel. Using both hands at once, he dropped the ribbon into the twin slots. When he was done there wasn't the slightest trace of ink on his finger tips.

The time Stapenell spent on HH 5166247 totaled about two and a half hours. He ran a sheet of paper into the machine and wrote out a test sample, checking the work of the aligning department. Finally he screwed the crackle-finished side, back and top covers in place, and fastened down the dust protectors at either end of the carriage. Just to make absolutely sure, he put the tension scales on the carriage a second time. The carriage moved, under his pull, at two pounds right on the nose. He opened and closed the pop-up top cover several times trying the latch on the push-button release. The catch was slightly out of line. He fixed it with a screwdriver, and tried it again. It popped as it should pop. Finally Stapenell pulled open the drawer of his desk and took out HH 5166247's papers. Before he fastened them onto the carriage, he took a large pencil with a soft lead and, on the workman's signature tag, in the space opposite "Operation C-40," he wrote a large, eminently legible, number "92."

Although he is not exactly upset about it, Stapenell is bothered by his belief that comparatively few persons, even among regular typewriter users, understand that the machine is a pre-

The Paper Roller Is Ground Down to Exact Diameter Speci-
fications

cision instrument, capable of great flexibility, adjustable in al-most every respect to within fine limits. There is some evidence that Stapenell may be correct.

There is, for instance, a story about a certain typewriter company that once received a sizzling letter of complaint from a man in Kansas City. The man had bought a new standard and had owned it a couple of months. His letter began with a burst of unprintable profanity, and continued in the same vein for several paragraphs. The most restrained remark the Kansas City man made was, "Yours is absolutely the worst typewriter I have ever seen in my whole life."

Since typewriter manufacturers worry about what customers think, the firm shot back an apologetic letter. It asked the man to send the offending machine right back to the factory for a checkup. But, the letter continued, one of the firm's experts had been studying the typing in the letter of complaint, and had come to the conclusion that perhaps all the machine needed was some adjustment, for the printing looked as if it might be the work of a very large, very tall man pounding the keys very hard and using a machine adjusted for a light-fingered touch-system operator.

The Kansas City man's answer, beautifully typed, reached the firm in about ten days:

> Dear Sirs: Is my face red? I stand six foot one inch in my stocking feet and I weigh 290 pounds. I use one finger of each hand, and I guess I belt the keys pretty hard. I've had the machine adjusted. It works perfectly. Apologies. . . .

12 / Quality Counts

For most persons, typewriter quality—a most complicated matter involving many separate elements—boils down to one simple, pay-off question: "How good does the writing look?"

The aligners in any typewriter factory spend all their time concentrating on this specific point. Typing's appearance depends upon the position of each letter within its printing space. All the little rascals should stand up far straighter than West Point cadets on parade, look as if their feet were firmly planted on the ground, and make a trim, smart-looking procession of well-integrated words across the page. The length and shape of the type bars are the variables. The type slugs themselves are soldered onto the business ends of the bars. Once they're on, they're set. When a letter is printing out of the proper position, the aligner shortens, lengthens or bends the type bar.

Each of the type slugs follows its own route to the printing point and each type bar has its own shape, like each of the irons in a set of matched golf clubs. Some are simple. The letters

"H-h," for instance, share a type bar that is pivoted almost directly below the printing point, and it's a flat, honest-looking affair because all it has to do is swing straight up, print what it has to print, and fall back into its position of rest with its head on its rubber pillow. Slugs like "Q-q" or "@-¢," on the other hand, come slithering over to the printing point from the extreme left and right, respectively, and their type bars have wicked elbow turns in them. They look, as they move, as if they were never going to straighten up in time. Yet they make it all right, and an innocent might never suspect, looking at a word like "quash," how much more the first letter had been through than the last.

Aligners have a secret seven-word sentence for testing typewriters' typing. It's not, "The quick brown fox jumps over the lazy dog," nor, "Now is the time for all good men to come to the aid of their party," but the meaningless—and yet provocative— "Amaranath sasesusos Oronoco initiation secedes Uruguay Philadelphia." An "amaranth" with only three "a"s, according to Webster, is an "imaginary, unfading flower" used poetically; possibly aligners in the beginning had this in mind and simply added the fourth "a" for their own purposes. "Sasesusos" is not a word at all, despite its beguiling lilt. It makes no difference. Although an aligner, seated before a typewriter, rips off this sentence almost automatically, he never tries to say it, and he seldom, if ever, thinks about its meaning. Each of the seven words has a special reason for being, and taken as a group they combine to show up a poorly aligned typewriter in a flash.

There are quite a few consonants sandwiched between repeated vowels ("ama," "ara," "ono," "oco," "ece," "ede" and so forth), and that's a tough alignment test. The pseudo-word

---

Steel-Treating Ovens Where Heated Parts Are Tempered in Oil

"amaranath" gives the letter "a," in particular, a chance to show itself. Should "a" or capital "A" be out of position—striking too far to the left or right, or too high or low, or canted on any oblique—the machine will write a sick-looking "amaranath." Furthermore, if upper-case and a lower-case samples are typed one immediately above the other

AMARANATH
amaranath

the aligner's practiced eye can immediately see the nature of "a"s ills, both in kind and degree. "Oronoco" checks the vowel "o" as critically as "amaranath" checks "a." "Secedes," "initiation" and "Uruguay" concentrate on "e," "i" and "u" respectively. "Sasesusos" gives "s" a workout against four of the five vowels, and includes several of the most common letter combinations in twentieth-century business English.

"Philadelphia" is in a special category. One aligning requisite is to persuade the reader's eye that the typed words are neatly closed up, like words printed on a printing press. Which is hard to do, because on the typewriter the narrow letters—"i," "l" and "t," for instance—tend to leave a mite too much white space around themselves, just as the wide letters like "w" and "m" are likely to crowd their neighbors. Every character, down to the mere (.) full stop, is allowed just as much space as each of the others, because that's the way the typewriter carriage moves. A Linotype machine, by contrast, uses from twelve to seventeen different letter-space widths when it sets type for printing, and the slug for "i" is a mere sliver compared to "w." Typewriting, to use the technical phrase, is not proportionately spaced, and if it were—so that seven-letter words, for example, would vary in length according to how many fat letters they included—

stenographers would be utterly miserable whenever they hit the wrong letter or typed the wrong word, because erasures and substitutions would be so much more difficult. (Nevertheless, the major companies are working furiously on experimental proportional-spacing typewriters instead of declaring, arrogantly, that it doesn't make sense except for those who want to use a typewriter as a substitute Linotype. Who knows? Maybe the market is filled with persons who want to do precisely that. One model of IBM's electric typewriter types semi-proportionally; it employs, that is to say, four different letter-space widths in the place of the customary one.)

Because the typewriter gives thin letters as much space as thick ones, "Philadelphia" is a problem word. The "il" combination may be beautiful. The "el" may appear as a model of neatness. But if the "l," perhaps, is ever so slightly off to the left of its space—the complete word may look awful. The aligner is likely to find that the "Philadel" has withdrawn itself from the "phia," a highly undesirable secession.

An aligner begins alignment with the letters "N-n." If he is alloted forty-five minutes for the complete job, he may spend the first ten minutes getting "N-n" perfectly positioned within its printing space. Or even longer, if he runs into trouble. There's no sense going on to the second letter until "N-n" is right, however long that takes, because it is the keystone of the operation. According to an aligners' maxim, "A man who hurries his "n"s will have to go back and do the job all over."

"N" is awarded this signal distinction because it's near the center of the keyboard, where the type bars are flat and straight and therefore least amenable to adjustment; and because "N" is a wide, tall, boxy capital that comes close to filling out the entire area in question. If one writes upper-case "N," underscores it, and puts it beneath an underscore in the space above, like this,

$$\overline{\text{N}}$$

one gets a fair picture of the full printing space. Furthermore, "N"'s serifs (the doodads on its feet and at the tops of the vertical strokes) are like rulers, in both upper and lower case, when "N"s or "n"s are juxtaposed with the other letters of the alphabet (NANBNCNDNE or nfngnhninjn). They help check horizontal straightness. That's how the aligner proceeds; he juxtaposes the other letters, the numerals and the punctuation marks against "N" and "n."

If he is working on "G," for example, he writes "NGN" and "ngn." He looks at the results suspiciously, and then, if he has spotted a fault, he makes a correction in the shape of the type bar with one of twenty tools designed for bending, squeezing, pinching, nipping and crimping. If "G" is low, the aligner can lengthen the type bar by squeezing. If "G" is tilted to the right, he can straighten it by bending. And so forth. The type bar is extraordinarily tough. It is carbon steel, which has been tempered with elaborate care and then drawn, so that its hardness— its ability, let's say, to resist penetration by a diamond-tipped drill—varies along its length. The shank end, where it is pivoted in the segment, is the hardest part. It's just about as hard as carbon steel can get. The softest part is near the type slug, or printing end. But the "soft" end is soft only by comparison with the hard end, and, in the best type bars, there is also a corrugation along the length of the bar to give it extra rigidity. Even in the worst of typewriters, type bars practically never break. Good type bars bend only under serious mistreatment, like repeated and forceful jamming over a long period of time. Their strength, in one way, makes the aligner's job tough, for he spends

Soldering Type onto the Type Bars

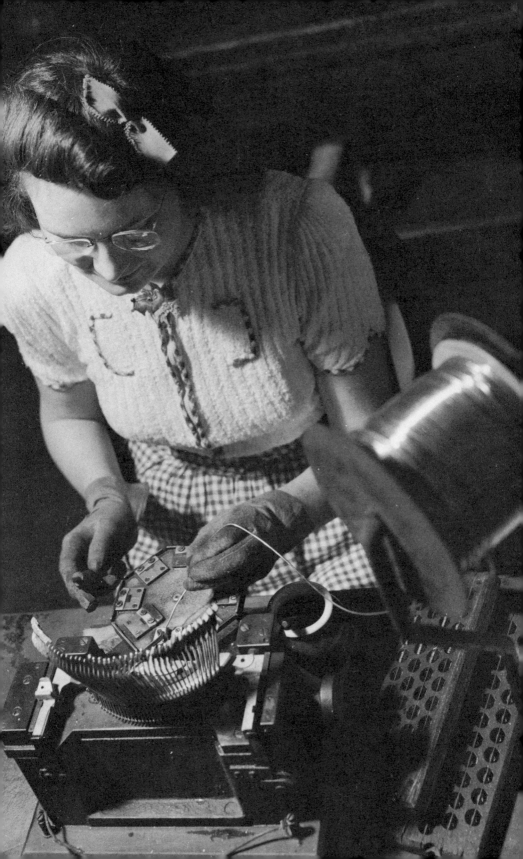

his life bending bars that are built to resist bending. His tools are no bigger than ordinary household pliers, but their names are indicative of their power. One, for instance, is called the "throwover." Another is the "mauler." On the other hand, because type bars *are* tough, a perfect alignment, once achieved, stays perfect through months, at least, of the most frenetic typing.

At the end of forty-five minutes, an expert aligner should have pinched and squeezed all the letters and characters into what appears, to his eye, as lovely position. He then writes out a complete sample, called a "strike-up" on a half sheet of typewriter paper:

```
N"N#N$N%_ N&N'N(N)N*N¼N@N:N?NN,N+N
n2n3n4n5n6n7n8n9n0n-n½n¢n/n,n. n=n    1234567890.


NANBNCNDNENFNGNHNINJNKNLNMNONPNQNRNSNTNUNVNWNXNYNZN
nanbncndnenfngnhninjnknlnmnonpnqnrnsntnunvnwnxnynzn

AMARANATH SASESUSOS ORONOCO INITIATION SECEDES URUGUAY PHILADELPHIA
amaranath sasesusos oronoco initiation secedes uruguay philadelphia
```

He delivers this strike-up to the desk of an inspector called the "marker." If the aligner has done well, and his vision of the ideal matches the marker's, the sample gets an okay, and the machine moves out of the aligning department to adjusting. Or, if the marker sees flaws, he marks corrections on the sample, like a proofreader marking printed matter, and the aligner has to give the faulty letters another small squeeze, a pinch or a bend.

The idea that an expert mechanic like an aligner should spend three-quarters of an hour on one typewriter is only slightly less shocking than the idea that the final adjuster may spend as long as three. Efficiency experts are invariably aghast. A good many of them, in the past, have felt more than confident that they

could save some of this time. Gadgets galore have been devised
and tested, all of them attempts to substitute machines for aligners' hands, aligners' eyes, and aligners' judgments.

So far the experiments have not worked out for precisely the
same reason that Stapenell is in no immediate danger of losing
his job to an electronic computer. Alignment is a matter of
judgment, and machines don't make judgments in anything approaching the human sense. The latest, most up-to-date way of
testing a musical instrument—a piano, for example—is to have
a man with a good ear play on it. The last word in examining
a typewriter for writing ability is to have a man with a good eye
write on it.

That exasperating fact brings up another technician who is,
simultaneously, half (or more) artist. He's the man who designs
typewriter type.

When typewriting looks good, it's because the aligner has
nursed the type bars into printing the type slugs almost exactly
as their type designer planned it.

Pica and élite are the two oldest, most common typewriter
type styles, familiar to all literates the world around. That has
a great deal to do with their satisfactoriness. They look like old
friends.

In design, pica and élite are much alike. Usually pica is
larger, so that a good many buyers order it when all they meant
to say was that they wanted big type (ten characters to the
inch) rather than little type (twelve characters to the inch).
The correct term for size, in typewriter language, is "pitch," a
measure of letter-space width and a sloppy word because it
doesn't tell, definitely, how tall the letters are. Sixteen letter-
spaces to the inch is ordinarily the smallest type available. Six
is the largest, not counting a special type for TV scripts which

can be read at twenty feet and has letters half an inch high but requires a special twenty-nine-key machine. You can have pica in the smaller size, 10 pitch, and élite comes in 12 pitch. Furthermore, each of the big-name machines offers lots of type faces besides pica and élite, often in two or more sizes. Some of the names of the more popular styles are Ampli, Book, Bulletin, Century, Executive, Gothic, Microtype, Monoface, Old English, Primer, Roman, Script and Vogue, among many others. Every company follows its own nomenclature and numbering system, which makes for some confusion, especially since one style may have several sub-styles. Among the picas, for instance, are Pica Intermediate, Pica Italic, Pica Multigraph, Pica Small, Pica Standard, Pica Distinctive, Pica Large, Pica Special, Pica Cloister and Pica Inverted. Each has a distinct personality all its own. The sensible way out of bewilderment, for the average buyer, is to ask for a chart of the type styles in their various sizes, and then just to point at the one he likes.

There are several hundred different type styles altogether, but if you don't like any of them (and are willing to foot the bill) you can have a private design of your own, as a good many firms have done. Dun & Bradstreet had Royal create a distinctive face, called Elite Semi Gothic 12 Pitch, to use for its business reports. Prudential Insurance's special order, a custom-designed face called Modified Pru Double Gothic 12 Pitch, was such a hit that it may now be had by anybody on any one of the major companies' machines; and a handsome, supremely legible type it is, especially for those with a good many insurance policies to type. Royal's Old English 9 Pitch was initially a special job for Keen's English Chop House, a restaurant on West Thirty-sixth Street, New York City. It's ideal for typing menu

---

Matrix Cutting. The Matrix Is the Pattern for the Type Dies

descriptions of double loin lamb chops or (if you don't happen to sell lamb chops) for diplomas, graduation certificates and Sunday School bulletin-board announcements.

Type designers are not only working constantly on such variations from classic printing types but on foreign-language designs, too. The fifty-odd languages that use the Roman alphabet (Danish, German, French, Portuguese, Greek, Serbian, etc.) are comparatively simple, for each letter stands by itself. Where the letters must be joined, or where local districts have their own strong opinions about how letters and symbols should be shaped, as in Arabic, Burmese, Hebrew, Siamese, Urdu and Marathi, the designer's headaches increase. And, when he tries to cope with Chinese, Japanese or Korean, he is very nearly stopped dead in his tracks. As if language problems were not trouble enough, type also must be sketched, drawn, die-cut and pressed for the special signs and symbols of special occupations: weather forecasting, chemistry, mathematics, science, check-writing, and music composing, to name just a few.

Whether the designer is working on Urdu or sixteenth-notes, he must keep one thought in mind: the stuff has got to be readable. It makes his task hard, because he is never allowed to proceed very far from what has already been. If he soars off on his own free fancy, and designs a beautiful letter "a" that looks rather like an ampersand (&), his artistic soul may be delighted, but his employers are going to be sore. Legibility is essential. Readers can only read words that look a lot like what they're accustomed to.

On the other hand, the designer must cook up something new. That's what he's paid for. Prudential would have been furious, if, for instance, its custom-styled type couldn't have been distinguished from the old stand-bys on Equitable's and Metropolitan's typewriters. As one distinguished designer once explained this fundamental craft dilemma, "It's like being a chef who is asked to do roast beef. A fancy name for the dish is a simple matter. But the meat itself, cooked the new way, has got to taste exactly like roast beef."

Typewriter-type designers, in contrast to printing-type designers, are further bound to the rigidity of set spacing: the "w"s they draw must fill the same paper area as their "i"s, and the words must look like integrated words, not just a casual grouping of isolated letters standing around in the same general locality. The serifs on the naturally narrow letters in pica and élite, for fatness, are wide. The base on the pica letter "i" is about as broad as the letter is tall—which is part of pica's typewriter charm. An ambitious young designer, however, is not likely to make a great name for himself by simply restyling good old pica. When he moves over into the general field of the Gothic, where serifs are miniscule or entirely missing, and "i"s are a mere vertical stroke, he begins to breathe with increased difficulty. A delightful sans-serif alphabet that looks fine on his drawing board may seem absurd by the time it has been cast and tried as a paragraph of actual typing. Considering all these hazards and restrictions, it's surprising that the industry has turned up numbers of men who can, and have, designed new typewriter type faces of real distinction. J. A. Hammel of Royal, W. A. Heiderich of IBM, Torsten Baudin of Underwood, and Floyd Adams of Remington Rand are among the many names on the list.

The invention of a machine to write Chinese has challenged typewriter men for a long time. The type-design difficulties are in themselves horrendous; but they have been overshadowed by the technical pitfalls in the way of building a machine to use the type. The English-writing typewriter was barely off the ground when inventors began to worry about the possibilities

Lin Yutang Watching His Daughter Type on the Machine He Invented

of a Chinese version, partly in the spirit of youthful geometry students who invariably take a crack at squaring the circle. By 1906, in an exclusive interview in *Typewriter Topics,* an experimenter named Kang Ye Wei expressed confidence that an ordinary United States office standard could be adapted to Chinese; he was working on it and expected to have a model ready shortly.

The main difficulties that confronted Kang were a) the fact that Chinese characters represent whole words or ideas, and not just letters of an alphabet, and b) there are forty-three thousand characters. Kang's plan was to cut the number down, which was perfectly reasonable. A Chinese telegraph book allows only nine thousand of the forty-three thousand. Schoolchildren use dictionaries that contain not more than ten thousand. College dictionaries list as few as fifteen thousand. The rest of the characters are highly technical words, or obsolete forms no longer in current usage, or artistic variations. A businessman in China, with a business letter to type, could easily get along without twenty thousand or thirty thousand of the total number.

An engineer, Chou Hou-k'un, actually marketed a Chinese typewriter in 1911 bearing out the optimistic views Kang expressed five years earlier. Chou's machine was not completely satisfactory. While it printed a vast number of characters, it didn't print enough. The operator had to keep a small box alongside the typewriter filled with extras. Whenever he came to a word that was missing, he hunted for the character in the box, found the appropriate type slug, and fitted it into a slot for typing.

Among dozens of other experiments, the most remarkable, by far, is a recent brain child of the author Lin Yutang. Several experimental models have been built, and the fact that the machine has not yet been put on the market is as much China's fault as Lin's. It is a most ingenious invention. It prints five thousand characters. By combining them—printing one on top of another—its total word capacity is ninety thousand, or more than twice the necessary number. Yet it's not appreciably larger than an ordinary typewriter—although at retail it would have to cost a great deal more.

Lin's typewriter, called the Minghwai, is as much an automatic file system as it is a writing machine. Its five thousand pieces of type fit comfortably into a space no larger than a Quaker Oats container; they are mounted on revolving octagonal bars on six rotating wheels, a variation of the type-cylinder idea. But instead of having five thousand keys, one per character, the Minghwai has only sixty-four, plus eight big square-topped printing levers where the space bar would ordinarily be found. The sixty-four keys are arranged in five rows.

In order to find a given character and bring it to the printing point, the operator presses one key in the top three rows of thirty-six keys representing thirty-six kinds of character tops. Then he presses one key in the two bottom rows which represent twenty-eight different kinds of character bottoms. There are a total of 1008 possible top-and-bottom combinations.

Immediately all of the five thousand characters with tops-and-bottoms of the kind specified show up on a small enlarging screen that rises up behind the main cylinder. There may be just a couple. There are not more than eight in any case. The process is something like asking a clothing salesman to show his complete assortment of blue sports jackets with harmonizing gray slacks. The Minghwai trots out everything it's got and displays it on the little screen. The chances are very good that the selection will include precisely the character desired, because Lin has arranged it that way. If it does, the typist makes his final choice with one of the eight big keys. He pushes down the number one big key, for instance, and the number one character on the screen is pressed against the paper. Or, if none of the available characters is quite right (the operator may be a Chinese poet looking for a word that hasn't been used since the Third Century B.C.) he forms a reasonably exact facsimile by printing two of them on top of each other.

The Minghwai, typing vertically, can do fifty characters a minute, according to the inventor's claim. On the pilot model, since its character capacity was even greater than necessary, Lin tossed in the English, Japanese and Russian alphabets for good measure and still had more than a thousand blanks left over. There's plenty of room left—if anyone wants to manufacture the thing—for esoteric scientific terms and a selection of subtle variants. And, in fact, if China only realized that Lin's Minghwai is waiting for her, she might very well overthrow her Soviet masters immediately.

Besides good alignment and good type design, there is a third, most critical element in a good strike-up: the ribbon. Hardly anyone appreciates the typewriter ribbon or its spiritual brother, the sheet of carbon paper. Seventy-seven companies, including the subsidiaries of the major typewriter-manufacturing firms, do close to a $50,000,000 business in ribbons and carbons. Thousands of persons work in their factories and distribute their products. Yet, with monumental injustice, most typists regard the ribbon as a nuisance and carbon paper as a messy, if necessary evil. What's even worse is their lack of understanding about the difference between good ribbons and bad ribbons, and their failure to see why top-quality carbon paper should cost more than the cheapest grade. It's odd that in the ribbons and carbons business, which is so intimately connected with the typewriter industry, price should often seem more important to buyers than quality. Yet a good many business houses that are glad to pay $100 more to buy the best machine balk at spending an extra 50 cents for a better ribbon. Even stenographers, who have always been so reliable in their typewriter preferences, sometimes fail to appreciate quality in supplies. The average typist, for instance, is not even aware that a ribbon needs rest to recuperate from the ordeal of having printed a letter. When the type strikes, it squeezes practically all the ink out of the ribbon and onto the paper. A first-class ribbon immediately begins to recover from the blow; ink from the surrounding fabric flows into the dry place and, by the next go-around, it's ready to make another impression as dark—or very nearly as dark—as the first. A ribbon will last as much as 20 per cent longer if, when the stenographer covers up her machine for the night, she will tighten the ribbon on its spools in order to enhance the ink-flow from one thickness of fabric to the next.

As far as beauty of the strike-up is concerned, it's important that the ribbon be as fine as possible. Some thickening and dulling of the letters is inevitable. If a line in the metal type is, say, two one-thousandths of an inch thick, the printed impression will be twice as wide at least. But if the ribbon is made of coarse material, and too heavily inked, and inked with an inferior grade of ink, the line can be five or six times as thick as the original, fuzzy on the edges, and, generally speaking, a smudge.

Typewriter-ribbon fabrics, whether cotton, nylon or silk, are more closely woven than any other kind of material; they are much finer, for instance, than parachute silk or the Byrd cloth used for skiers' jackets. A ribbon thread-count of three hundred per square inch is a commonplace, whereas balloon fabric is usually not more than 250 and percale sheets are from 180 to two hundred. The inks are tricky stuff, because they are expected to combine several qualities. They don't dry out for years as long as they're kept in their little boxes or while they're in place on the typewriter. They are only slightly susceptible, in other words, to oxidization. And yet, ideally, the typed impression should be completely dry—by absorption alone—within a few seconds after it hits the paper. If you're using a top-quality ribbon, the first letter in a typed line will be dry before you've reached the right-hand margin. You can erase, or run your finger across it, without getting any smear at all. Furthermore, the color mustn't fade, whether it is black or red or any of the dozen other hues now commonly available.

What burns up the scientists who have brought typewriter inks to their present high state of refinement is the popular confusion between darkness of impression and ribbon quality. There's nothing darker than a brand-new, very cheap ribbon. It throws excess ink all over the page. It is so black that the centers of the "e"s and "o"s are all filled in, and the margins of the page usually contain clear impressions of the typist's fingerprints. It's not initial blackness that determines how long a ribbon will last; it's ink and fabric quality. Most ribbons are cotton. A good cotton can be a very fine ribbon indeed. It has better ink-holding ability than nylon, because nylon threads are entirely non-absorptive and the ink merely rests in the cloth's interstices without being soaked up. But the best ribbons, which cost at least half again as much as good quality cotton, are silk. Silk ribbons have a limited popularity. Some local stationery stores don't carry them at all, and their proprietors may say that they never heard of such a thing. No matter what they say, most of the seventy-seven ribbons-and-carbons companies are making silk ribbons, and they can be ordered without any difficulty.

It behooves ribbon buyers to try silk, if only to relieve the frustrations of the chemists, fabric specialists and manufacturers who have poured their best efforts into this *ne plus ultra* item. Not to mention the fact that silk, in the long run, saves money. A top-grade cotton ribbon at about $1.50 retail will deliver a fairly good impression for 900,000 characters, or about a hundred and eighty thousand words. A silk, at about $2.85, is good for 2,300,000 impressions, or 460,000 words—partly because, ordinarily, it comes in an eighteen-yard length on the same-sized spool as the usual twelve-yard length of cotton. A medium-inked silk doesn't start as black as a very cheap ribbon made of cotton; too much ink is not consistent with sharp definition. But after a couple of hundred thousand words, the silk's impression remains almost as dark as it ever was. The fabric is extremely elastic and tough. Unless your automatic ribbon reverse is broken, the silk won't wear through until after the ink supply has been exhausted. Carbons are clearer. And, most important, the strike-up is as handsome as the wear on the type and the state of alignment will allow. All of which explains why 90 per cent of customers who've tried silk once buy it again the next time.

Carbon papers are coated with ink not unlike ribbon ink, but with an added ingredient, carnauba wax from Brazil. Its addition, early in the 1900's, revolutionized carbon papers. They used to be far more difficult to handle than they are now. Beeswax, lampblack and grease—the earliest coating formula—not only made an impossible mess, but the grease was soon absorbed by the paper. When carbons were only a few months old, whether they had been used or not, they were no longer any good. The carnauba-wax formula, after it cools and hardens, lasts a long time. Its surface, instead of being soft and sticky, is comparatively hard; it is a lot easier to handle and it also makes

---

Ink Processing Machine

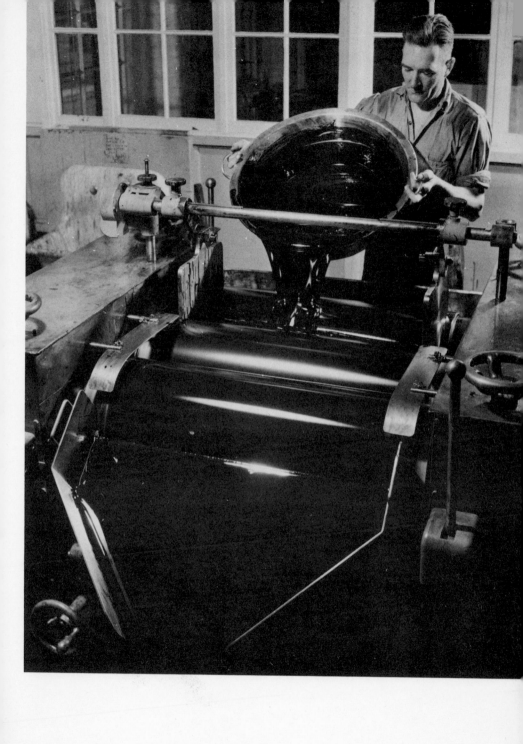

more copies of far greater clarity. A top-quality sheet of modern carbon paper should be good for at least fifty usings. Typewriter users seem inclined to save pennies on carbons in the same way that they are miserly about ribbons. For those who have never owned anything but the cheapest carbon paper, it may be news: curling in carbons was rendered obsolete some years ago, when it was discovered that the dreadful shortcoming could be eliminated by coating the non-inky side of the sheet with a very thin layer of plastic. Almost every first-class brand now comes with such an anti-curl coating.

The art of selling typewriters has undergone a comparable refining process. No one is positive that today's salesman outclasses his pioneer predecessor by as great a margin as the machine proper, but that's partly because, during the years 1946 to 1953, typewriters have been scarce rather than abundant; one firm has not yet caught up with the backlog of orders that mounted during World War II. As long as a man can earn commissions by simply answering the telephone and saying "I'll try to get them for you," he is not likely to demonstrate the full frenzy of his selling capabilities. Even without desperation as an incentive, 1954's typewriter company representative—a personable young man wearing a Dacron-blend suit, and in little danger of being mistaken for a peddler—is likely to have your name on a sales agreement long before you've had a chance to tell him that your old Oliver is still entirely satisfactory.

Some of his strategies are modern versions of time-honored gambits. He endeavors, initially, to get permission to leave one of his typewriters around your place. Before he goes away, however, he demonstrates its wonders to you (making sure that your typist also catches the act). Demonstration technique has a built-in manner of casualness, almost as if the lad were being carried along by the machine's intrinsic virtues, but his ap-

parent ease and confidence are as accidental as a stage performance by that master of acting detail, Miss Helen Hayes. Every
movement has been plotted, planned and studied for effect. The
first thing an apprentice salesman learns, after he has memorized
the name of the machine he's to sell, is the formal demonstration
technique. He goes to demonstration school, operated by the
company. He is not let loose until he is a proficient master of the
art; and even then, in all likelihood, he will, for a time, accompany an old hand for some months before he's allowed to make
a call all by himself. It's not typing *per se* that he learns (although ability to type is an asset) but how to make the particular
features of the particular machine glitter in the most favorable
light.

Since the demonstrator's audience regularly includes professional experts—namely, secretaries and typists—he is extremely
candid. He might be able to hoodwink business executives without too much trouble, but with experienced writing-machine
operators he hardly dares attempt more than the most delicate
hyperbole. He not only knows his own typewriter intimately,
but he tries to be as expert as possible on the other four, with
special emphasis, naturally, upon their foibles.

There's no telling how tough the questions put to him may
be. Not long ago, for instance, one well-known typewriter had
type bars that were not made out of tempered, drawn, carbon
steel, but just out of run-of-the-mill steel. That meant that a
salesman could put the shank end of the bar down on a desk
with its length projecting over the edge, give it a twang with
his finger, and produce a ringing note reminiscent of the whine
of a musical saw. Which is precisely what the firm's salesmen
were instructed to do—a bold effort to make a liability sound
like a virtue. In business offices all over the country dutiful
salesmen began twanging samples of their second-rate type

bars, beaming, and asking whether the competition dared try the same.

There was no answer to the twang-test propaganda except truth. It was not convincing to say, simply, that twanging-ability, in a type bar, is a symptom, *ipso facto,* of inferiority. The rival salesmen were compelled to bone up on the intricacies of type-bar design, types of steel, and steel processing as if they were students at the Massachusetts Institute of Technology. For they had to be able to give a coherent answer, without gulping or gawking, to the question, "Well, all right, but why don't your type bars whine?"

Although the girls in the office may make the decision about whether to buy or not to buy, salesmen understand perfectly well that the boss signs the papers and cannot be entirely ignored. Some of the most seductive of the typewriter man's arguments are reserved for executives' ears alone.

The salesman, for instance, who knows that his typewriter is the favorite among the girls, may close a deal when the time comes with an effective, basic line: "Of course I realize, sir, that you are too busy to care much whether you buy one machine or another. But it means a lot to the secretaries. Why not settle it, in a minute, by taking a quick poll? If the vast majority votes for one typewriter, the sensible move is to standardize on it. . . ."

Another effective stratagem—especially when the boss seems to hesitate about the money he'll have to shell out—is the "typing station" approach, which is now popular among office-appliance salesmen generally.

"I'm sure you've got a fine typewriter there," the executive admits, "but, frankly, business has been lousy. We just can't afford to spend the money right now."

The salesman looks sympathetic, despite the fact that he rarely hears a businessman say anything else.

"Think of it this way," the salesman suggests. "Think of the secretary as the hub of a typing station, a unit, like any other part of your plant, turning out a product. The typing station produces your letters, your memorandums and your records. All right. It has one employee. You pay her $80 a week, roughly $4,500 a year counting bonuses, social security, health insurance and the rest. You spend another $1,000 on the stationery, stamps and supplies she uses. You pay rent on the office space for her desk, the file cabinet, and the space around them. Then there's her telephone bill and the electricity and the cost of maintaining her corner of the office. Let's say, speaking most conservatively, that this one typing station is costing $7,000 a year."

"At least that much," the businessman agrees.

"Well your return on that $7,000 investment depends entirely on the typewriter. The new machine will mean that the girl will be happy. She'll do more and better work. The efficiency of the typing station will be improved. And at a cost—considering the big, generous allowance I'm offering on your old machine—of not much more than a mere $125. At that price I don't see how you can afford not to buy."

Of all boss-directed sales talks, however, the most refined and subtle is the cost-analysis presentation for big offices with lots of typewriters. Most large companies have a set policy about typewriter replacements; they turn in their old machines when they reach a prescribed age. Some companies keep the old warhorses going for as long as ten or fifteen years or even longer, for there's nothing about an antique typewriter that can't be repaired or replaced, just as an ancient automobile, for a price, can be kept running presumably forever.

Typewriter service costs naturally increase with the machine's age. This fact, plus the dwindling size of turn-in allowances, and tax deductions for business-equipment expenses, and a few other comparable factors, means that a good many typewriter users are actually losing money by running their machines longer than they should. Any such outfit is a salesman's meat.

He works out a cost analysis for the company's executives which shows all the factors involved in a decision to buy or not to buy.

The tricky part of the technique is this: if the firm is well past the economic turn-in point, the salesman *deliberately understates his case.* He never reports that new machines will save the company 2 cents per day per typewriter, even if that's true. He shows, instead, that the cost of new machines is only a trifling additional amount—presuming that the prospect will agree that getting so much for so little is indeed a bargain. He may make a sale on that point alone.

But ordinarily the businessman, going over the figures, sees that the salesman has left out a factor or two on the savings side. With a whoop of delight, the comptroller rushes into the boss's office, shouting, "Holy smoke! If we buy those new typewriters, we'll actually be saving money!" From that point on, needless to say, the signing of the contract is a mere formality.

For all of the contemporary salesman's Machiavellian tricks, he has a most difficult time unless his typewriter is well built. If there is anything wrong with the product and the customers fail to spot it right away on their own, the salesmen from the four other companies will point it out soon enough. Quality therefore is much more than the machine's appearance, the neatness of the print, or the color of the finish. And it goes beyond obvious matters like the convenience of the controls, or the eye-catching advantages of the various time-saving and energy-conserving gadgets. If one thinks of entering the typewriter field as a manufacturer, just now, and with any plan of beating the leaders at their own game, he must be prepared to achieve and maintain quality throughout the manufacturing process, from buying the raw materials to fastening the big babies inside their shipping cases. Then—but not before then— he can worry about an improved handbook of strategies for his salesman.

The phrase "quality control" is a watchword around today's typewriter factory—as it is, to be sure, in a good many other industries where precision is a prime requisite. Not many of the mechanical gadgets in common use, however, have as many working parts as a typewriter, or as many close adjustments. Of those that do, few are sold, like typewriters, with a year's guarantee. Still fewer will last—with minor servicing—for twenty years. "Quality control" means that the man in charge of the typewriter factory, assisted by an army of from five hundred to a thousand lieutenants, has got to keep management's nose in everything all the time to make sure that each of the thousands of operations is being performed right up to snuff, both by the men and by the machines. Every employee on the payroll has got to be taught that the company would rather do almost any-thing, regardless of cost, than ship a defective typewriter; for no amount of inspection and checking can keep quality up to specifications unless the entire plant understands that quality is the Big Idea. It also means that your factory, big brute that it is, can be intimidated by one letter from one dealer, let's say. in Spokane, who writes to say that twice, within a single month, he's received machines with sticky type bars.

The first thought that flashes through the manager's brow is this: "If Spokane has had two cases of sticky type bars, per-haps Seattle has had six. And heaven help the company if sticky type bars are epidemic!"

Needless to say, the manager has not gotten to be head of the factory by losing his head in emergencies. He does not immediately give up the ship as lost. But neither does he scoff at Spokane's criticism—far from it. He investigates. The Spokane dealer may be wrong, of course. The factory calls in and examines the offending typewriters, when that's possible. At least it checks, via the machines' serial numbers, to see who assembled the type bars, aligned them, adjusted them, and inspected these operations, and whether anything could have gone wrong anywhere in the process.

The assumption is, that with all the precautions in the world, something may have gone wrong. The certainty is that, if there has been trouble, it's far less expensive to call back all typewriters after a given serial number than to let the public buy them and be disappointed.

If, after investigation, there seems to be no fault, and provided that there are no more complaints, the factory breathes easily again, and the manager resumes his normal eight hours of untroubled sleep.

If there is a fault, it must be corrected. Immediately after the introduction of a new model typewriter—or, less likely, but conceivably at any time—a dealer, a customer, or anyone else might have a criticism that couldn't be answered except by an actual change in the machine; a complaint, in other words, about design rather than about some accident in the manufacturing process. Quality control, as the term is used by the best typewriter companies, covers such criticism. It seems close to unbelievable, yet it is literally true, that several customer beefs, combined with an idea about how to improve the matter, will change the machine within a few weeks' time.

That doesn't happen very often, of course.

Usually the complaints that are valid—and there are not many of them—can be traced back to some simple human error. One man on assembly has unconsciously developed a minor bad habit like turning a set screw half a revolution too far, or something of the sort.

Not long ago the Royal factory, which holds its major quality-control meeting every Tuesday morning at ten-thirty, was baffled by reports from dealers that some standards were arriving with the big screws that hold them inside their packing cases perilously loose. No one could figure out why. The screws themselves were first quality. There'd been no change in the method for years, and never before had a complaint on that particular score been received. Yet the word kept coming in. There was no doubt that for some mysterious reason those screws weren't holding. Royal inspectors haunted the packing room for days until someone noticed that one of the men who put the screws in place was a lot shorter than any of the others. Because of his height, he had trouble reaching up to the top ones, and he was forced to hold his screwdriver at a slightly cockeyed angle.

The quality-control committee thought hard. Someone had an inspiration: give the short man a box to stand on.

If you want to manufacture typewriters, you must steel yourself for meeting and surmounting crises of that sort. Loose screws can lead to damaged typewriters, damaged typewriters can lead to stenographer disfavor—and stenographer favor, as all typewriter men after Wyckoff, Seamans and Benedict have known, is what you've got to have.

The three and a half million professional typists, for all their casualness about putting the covers on their machines before they go home to dinner, are an exacting board of typewriter examiners. Secretaries may not show any special interest in carbon steel or aluminum castings, yet they decide, in the last analysis, precisely what typewriters are to be. They like their writing machines to be good. They vote unanimously for quality. They cannot be denied.

Index

About the Author

BRUCE BLIVEN, JR., was born in Los Angeles, but left California at the age of sixteen months and has lived in New York ever since. He wrote briefly for the Stroudsburg, Pa., *Record* and for the world-famed *Manchester Guardian*. After graduating from Harvard he was an editorial writer on the New York *Post*, which he left to serve in World War II. When he returned to civilian life he started work as a free-lance magazine writer.

A member of the Society of Magazine Writers, he has done articles for *Life, Esquire, Woman's Home Companion, The New Yorker* and more than twenty other magazines. Mr. Bliven's father is an editor of *The New Republic* and his wife is in the editorial department of a leading New York book publishing firm.